ANGEL DUSTED

Angel Dusted

A FAMILY'S NIGHTMARE

Ursula Etons

MACMILLAN PUBLISHING CO., INC.

NEW YORK

This is a work of non-fiction. All of the people, the places, and the events depicted are real. Only the names have been changed to protect the principals.

Macmillan Publishing Co., Inc.
866 Third Avenue, New York, N.Y. 10022
Collier Macmillan Canada, Ltd.

Library of Congress Cataloging in Publication Data
Etons, Ursula.
Angel dusted
1. Phencyclidine abuse—United States—Biography.
2. Psychoses—United States—Biography. 3. Etons,
Ursula. I. Title.
RC568.P45E76   362.2'93'0926 [B]   79-18915
ISBN 0-02-536600-9

First Printing 1979
Printed in the United States of America

Excerpt from "Scent of Irises" is from *The Complete Poems of D. H. Lawrence*. Copyright © 1964 by Angelo Ravagli and C. M. Weekley, Executors of the Estate of Frieda Lawrence Ravagli. Excerpted by permission of Viking Penguin, Inc.

Excerpt reprinted from Sylvia Plath's *The Bell Jar* by permission of Harper & Row.

For my children—my raison d'être

—And yes, thank God, it still is possible—
The healing days shall close the darkness up
. . . Now . . . the golden fire has gone,
and your face is ash—

—D. H. LAWRENCE
"Scent of Irises"

CONTENTS

ACKNOWLEDGMENTS

To my dear friend and mentor, writer Mike McGrady, warmest thanks for your advice and encouragement.

To Captain Donald White, Chief of the Narcotics Division, Nassau County Police Department, thank you for the technical information on drugs.

To Dr. Leslie Lukash, Nassau County Medical Examiner, many thanks for the medical information you provided.

ANGEL DUSTED

1

OF MADNESS

HANG TOUGH—BUT BE MELLOW.
The sign was hand-lettered on a large cardboard and placed
above his bed. I remembered the sign that morning . . . and
took it down . . . and placed it very carefully in the bottom of
my desk drawer. Owen had written it last summer—for himself.
But it helped me get through that awful day and all the days
thereafter . . .

It was a sleepy Sunday. A sunny autumn Sunday. Luxuriating
in the warmth of new sheets I thought of the day ahead. Nothing
to do but think of nothing. Should I make brunch or feign sleep?
What a relief just to be able to stretch out and relax. I heard
Vincent puttering clumsily about in the tiny kitchen. He must
be feeding the cat, I assumed. Then again, he could be feeding
himself. So much the better. I braved a glance at the digital clock.
10:01. Who cared. There was nothing to do. It was Sunday.
I had free time on my hands and it was all mine. I rolled over,
pulling the fluffy pillow over my ears, hardly hearing the soft
ring of a telephone. Somewhere . . .

Ten on a Sunday morning . . . who would call? Bad form.
I tried not to listen, nose buried downward, as Vincent, my
husband, answered in the kitchen.

"Owen" came through the Sunday-morning stillness. "Owen" . . . my son's name was being repeated.

"Owen?" my husband was saying. "Where? When did this happen?"

There was something amiss. I sat up and reached for the extension phone beside the bed.

"What is it?" I came awake. "What happened? Who is this?" Visions of my son, lying broken and bleeding, passed before my eyes.

"Owen is ill," a strange voice informed me. "He's here in my office. This is Dr. Martin, the university psychologist." His voice was too pleasant for the message he was delivering. "Your son was brought to my office a little while ago by security—"

"Security! What are you talking about?" I impatiently interrupted.

"Your son doesn't know what he's doing. He seems to have had a breakdown—"

"You can't be serious!"

"Mrs. Etons, security found Owen running through the dormitory halls with a fire extinguisher in his hands. He appears to be quite manic, quite incoherent and disoriented at the moment. We're going to have to send him home. At this point it looks as though he's going to need hospitalization."

"I don't understand. It can't be . . . it can't be Owen."

"Mrs. Etons," the voice was firmer now, "Owen is in a manic state. He's agitated. I know it's hard for you to accept but he's ill—and he's going to need immediate treatment. In a hospital."

"We'll come up for him," Vince said on the other phone.

"No, that won't be necessary," Dr. Martin stated, now soothingly. "He's asked to have his brother drive him home. We called and he's on his way here now." (Marc was at a neighboring upstate university.)

I hung up the phone and looked out, numbly, at the now harsh, bright October sky.

I turned to Vincent as he entered the bedroom, his boyish face gone haggard. "I can't understand this. Maybe . . . maybe I could . . . if Owen had been a different kind of person. If

. . . if he had been a problem child, if he had caused us concern. But he's always been so good—so loving—so well adjusted. A beautiful angel. An angel."

"Cut it out, Ursula. Talking this way isn't going to solve anything. We're going to have to get a doctor."

Cool-headed Vince. Outwardly unperturbed. I admired him then as he picked up my personal telephone directory.

"Who are you calling?"

"Who would be a better person to call than Hank Brenner." Hank. Of course. Our dear friend and internist.

"But it's Sunday. He might be sleeping!"

"I know it's Sunday. But our kid is sick and we have to get the name of a psychiatrist in the area. Now, just let me call him."

The line was busy. Vince put the receiver down. I put my hand on his. "Look, why don't you go and put on a pot of coffee. Let me talk to Hank." I wanted to discuss Owen with him myself. After all, it was such a delicate situation. By sheer reason of motherhood, I felt better able to explain. Better able to ask for help . . .

Hank Brenner gave me the phone numbers of three local psychiatrists. He was sensitive enough not to ask for details.

I began making the calls. The first doctor was sorry, but he wasn't taking on any new patients. The second psychiatrist also had a closed practice, but he seemed concerned and was willing to talk to me. He asked questions.

"Does your son take drugs?"

Drugs? Owen? What was he talking about?

"It's hard for me to even think of drugs," I replied, as lightly as possible. "Why, we don't even smoke cigarettes in this household."

"Well, Mrs. Etons, drugs are now a fact of life on every college campus," he stated bluntly. "You tell me that your son has always been happy and well adjusted, that he's always been an outstanding student, and frankly I can think of only one logical explanation—drugs."

Drugs. The thought disturbed me. I queried Vincent.

"Anything is possible, Ursula. The doctor must know the

current situation. Now, c'mon, get the other guy on the phone."

The third psychiatrist said yes, he would see Owen. Would I please bring him over tomorrow evening at six.

"Tomorrow evening? But, doctor, you don't seem to realize how very sick he is! The school psychologist said he will need immediate treatment—"

"Mrs. Etons, that's the only opening I have for tomorrow."

I hung up. Did I have any choice?

Walking around our garden apartment, I tried to think things through. But there was no explanation. Not yet. The doctor said drugs. But then I thought of sweet Owen, his soft handsome face, pale blue eyes, blond hair, always a pleasant smile, always a kind word. Drugs? No, I was not ready to accept that yet. Perhaps it was just a temporary breakdown. Perhaps he could be treated at home. Perhaps . . . The phone rang. It was now three o'clock.

"Mom, it's Marc. Listen, we've just stopped for lunch. We're at the Rollingwood Diner. Marsha's with us. It'll be another couple of hours before we're home."

"How's your brother?"

"Well, he's kind of agitated."

"What do you mean?"

"He wants to talk—and he's rambling on—"

"Is he making any sense?"

"Not very often."

"What is he saying?"

"Well, he thinks we're riding in President Carter's motorcade."

"My God!"

"Look, I just called to let you know where we were. I didn't want you to worry."

"President Carter's motorcade . . . I can't believe that."

"Mom, are you all right?"

"I'm all right."

"Okay, then. We should be here for about an hour."

"Try to be home before dark."

"Well, I can't promise. It's a long trip."

"Yes, but try."

"Okay, Mom, we'll try."

"Take care."

I hung up the phone and went into the living room to speak to Vincent. The younger children, Suzy and Tim, were there, sitting on the rug, playing Monopoly. Somberly.

Vincent looked up from the *Times*. "What's the matter? You don't look right. Who was that on the phone?"

"It was Marc. They've stopped for lunch. They're in Rollingwood."

"Good. I'm glad they were sensible enough to stop for food."

"Vince—"

"What?"

I wanted to tell him about the "motorcade" but I looked at Suzy and Tim and thought better of it. "Oh, nothing." Suddenly I felt very tired. "I just wanted to tell you that I'm going in to lie down."

I went into the bedroom, kicked off my slippers, and lay down. My head was beginning to throb slightly. Sleep would be beneficial; it would prevent a tension headache.

It was dusk when I awoke. The place was remarkably quiet even though I knew that they would all be sitting in the next room. Waiting. I sat up on the edge of the bed. My body felt heavy. Wooden. I slid my feet into my furry slippers.

The phone rang. The ring jarred me. I grabbed for it quickly. It was Marc again. They were still at the diner.

"What time is it?" I demanded.

"It's five o'clock."

"Five o'clock! But you said you'd be leaving in an hour."

"We were going to, Mom." His voice pleaded. "But Owen wanted to talk. So we stayed here for a while."

"Talk . . . about what?"

"About school. About pressure. About a lot of things."

"What do you mean, pressure?"

"Well, you know, things are rough at that university."

"I see."

"Anyway, we're getting ready to leave now. I just wanted to let you know."

"Please come straight home. It's getting so late—"

"Sure, Mom."

"And now you'll be home in the dark—"

"It just can't be helped, Mom. Now, please don't worry."

"Will one of you sit in the back with Owen—just in case—" I thought of the madness of that morning, the wild run through the dorm.

"Sure, Mom. Marsha's driving. My better half's a better driver than me. I'll sit in the back with Owen. It'll be okay. He thinks we're still in Carter's motorcade, anyway."

"Oh, God!"

"I told him Carter's heading for a speaking engagement in New York."

"Enough!"

"Don't worry, Mom. You just take it easy."

"Tell Marsha to take it easy—please."

"Okay. See you later, Mom."

I put the receiver down and lay back on the bed once more. *Owen wanted to talk . . . about school . . . about pressure . . .* Unpleasant thoughts intruded. The chronic money problems. The large house we had to sell in Marsey County because the taxes were too high. The divorce. The flight to Florida. Then Timmy, age twelve, spending the summer with me and wanting me to come back to Long Island. . . . The return. And then the remarriage to Vincent only eight months after the divorce. Just one month ago, to the day. Funny. It was our anniversay today. A day of celebration.

I thought of Vincent in the next room. He was probably still reading the Sunday *Times;* the business section, no doubt. Imperturbable. Composed. Silent. That was the trouble with Vincent, I concluded. Totally undemonstrative. And yet, he cried when Owen left for college. Owen had always been his favorite child.

Sweet, delightful Owen. Never a word of complaint. About the divorce. About the new house I had bought in sunny Florida; a rambling house, tucked into a quiet corner of the Palm Beaches. Driving me south last winter, the day after the divorce became final, Owen had sat behind the wheel of my sports coupe, as pleasant and charming as ever. But he was unusually subdued. I tried to make the adventure sound exciting.

"You'll like the house. It's bright and airy. And, oh yes, there's central air conditioning—and it's only a block away from golf and tennis."

"How about a built-in swimming pool?" he quipped.

"I can't afford a pool just yet. But you'll see. Someday we'll have a beautiful pool, all screened in, and you'll all enjoy it immensely."

"How can I enjoy it if I'm in the cold winter wilds of upstate New York?"

"You'll all come down for Christmas. And Easter, too. And think of the summers—"

"We'll see." The smile had turned to stony silence. . . .

Vincent came into the room.

"Who was that on the phone just before?"

"It was Marc again. They're just leaving the diner now."

"Why so late?"

"Owen wanted to talk . . . Vince?"

"What?"

"He thinks that they're in Carter's motorcade."

Silence. In the deepening semi-darkness I strained to see the expression on his lean, angular face, but it was a hazy blur. He slowly turned around and walked out of the room.

I dragged my body, stiff as a marionette, up off the bed and into the tiny kitchen.

Suzy came in to help.

"Mom," she whispered. "Owen's been smoking pot."

"How do you know?" I pounced on her.

"Cause he told me."

"When did he start? Where did he smoke it?"

"He started last summer. Before he went back to school. You know, when you were living in Florida."

"He didn't smoke it here, surely your father—"

"He smoked with his friends. Not here."

I mechanically mixed the tuna salad. I could not concentrate on preparing anything more complex.

"Suzy, I can't believe marijuana would make him so sick."

"I think he took speed, too."

I stared in disbelief at my seventeen-year-old daughter. Her casualness stunned me. I was at a loss for words.

She handed me the mayonnaise. I tried to be casual, too.

"Was he smoking pot—and taking—other things—last year, too?"

"He just started last summer."

Last summer. Of course. For his first year away at college had been so terrifically successful. But why? Why did he start last summer? And why did he continue? I wondered how much more Suzy knew.

"Was he smoking pot at school this year?"

"Are you kidding? Everyone smokes at *that* school!" (She had friends on the campus.)

As I set the table I glanced into the adjoining living room. Vince and Timmy were glumly engrossed in a game of chess. It was now quite dark, the darkness covering the picture window like a heavy blanket. An ominous chill was in the air. I quickly crossed over to the large window, closed it tightly, and pulled the shade down to the sill. Trying to shut out the dark. The cold. My thoughts.

Mrs. Etons . . . they found Owen running through the dormitory halls with a fire extinguisher in his hands. . . .

We sat down to our modest supper. None of us was hungry, but we ate. We cleaned our plates and tried to converse politely, for we are truly a family of stoics. We finished the meal. And we waited for the night. And for Owen.

2

THE ARRIVAL

They march up the stairs. It is a slow and solemn procession. Marsha, my daughter-in-law, first; then Owen, gaunt and staring; and finally Marc, carrying the suitcase.

Owen is different. I notice it in his eyes. They stare, but they do not see. Rosemary's Baby's eyes. Gleaming silver.

I direct Marc and the others into a bedroom with the suitcase. Kisses are perfunctory.

Owen must be observed. I return to him. His blond eyebrows are arched malefically over flashing eyes. He turns wordlessly away from me, glides into the living room and sits on the large pine rocker. As I stare in soundless disbelief, he lowers his trousers below his knees and takes out a box of contraceptives and leaves it on his lap. He continues to rock, eyes gleaming wildly. I quickly go over to him and help him pull his trousers up, taking the box of Trojans and slipping it into my apron pocket.

The rest of the family trickles slowly into the room. Marc looks extremely tired. Marsha is as bubbly and bouncy as ever.

"How was the trip?" I lamely ask. As Owen rocks. Mechanically.

"It was as smooth as can be," Marsha casually replies as she lights a Parliament, her first of many. I glance admiringly at my young, pretty daughter-in-law. Just twenty, and already married for two years. Too young.

"Mom, have you contacted a doctor?" Marc's thin face is tight-lipped. Older than its twenty-one years.

"Yes, but he can't see your brother until tomorrow evening at six. Isn't that ridiculous?"

"What can you do?" he wearily replies. "He's probably busy making the rounds at some hospital all afternoon."

Practical Marc. Just like his father.

We talk about the trip downstate. Matter-of-factly. Each of us trying not to notice Owen. Rocking silently. Like some baneful stranger from another planet. Another dimension.

"Would you like something to eat? Please?" I plead. "I've made a tuna salad, and there's some cheese."

"Okay, Mom," Marc readily accepts, "but not too much. We ate a lot at the diner."

We tell Owen to come to the table and he gets up and follows us. He still hasn't uttered a word.

I serve the salad and fill Owen's plate to the brim. But he doesn't eat. I am distressed for he always had such a good appetite. I keep urging. But he doesn't seem to hear. Finally I get him to drink a glass of Coca-Cola.

"Well." Marsha lights another cigarette, forcing nonchalance. "That was a super salad. Can I make some coffee?"

"It's made," I quickly reply, and bring the pot to the table.

"I'd like some coffee," Owen says. "I have to have coffee."

Pleased with his sudden response, I serve him before the others. He gulps the hot liquid down, gets up, and goes back into the living room. There he sits once more in the rocker. Gliding. Back and forth.

I bite my lip and turn to his older brother. "How long do you suppose he's been like this?"

"I don't know, Mom, he never calls me. He hasn't written to us in weeks. I honestly don't know." Marc cracks his knuckles. The sound startles me, unnerves me. I ask Marsha for a cigarette.

"Now, c'mon, Ursula," Vince admonishes me. "You know you stopped a long time ago."

"Yes, I know," I reply, wearily. I light up and take a long drag. The tobacco tastes awful but I am determined to relax—and to finish the cigarette.

"Did you get all of his things?" I turn to Marsha now.

"Yes. His roommate packed and left everything ready for us on his bed."

His roommate. "Did you have a chance to speak to Greg?" I ask, hopefully.

"No. He was nowhere in sight."

"Did you check all of his drawers? And his closet?"

"Everything. Oh—but—" Marsha hesitates.

"But what?"

"There was something else. On his dresser."

"Oh, forget it!" Marc interjects.

"Forget what?" I demand. "What did you leave on his dresser?"

"A pipe."

"A pipe?"

"A corncob pipe. We decided it would be best to leave it behind."

"I see."

"Well," Marsha gets up gracefully and pushes her chair under the table. "We really must be going now. We'll be staying with my folks tonight. It was a long trip and we've got to get some rest."

"When are you going back?" I ask.

"Tomorrow," Marc replies. "We'll both be missing a couple of classes."

"I'm sorry, Son," Vince says, putting his arm around Marc's shoulders. "We would have come up but Dr. Martin said you had already been called."

"Yeah, Dad. Owen asked for me."

Owen asked for me . . . I ponder that point. How irrational could he have been? . . .

Marc kisses me good-bye.

"Take it easy, Mom."

"I'll try."

"Good-night, Mom." Marsha gives me a hug.

It is now eleven o'clock. Tim and Suzy have already gone to bed. Tomorrow is a school day.

Owen rocks on. I look searchingly at Vincent.

"We ought to get him to bed," he says.

"Yes," I agree. "I'll get his bed ready and put his pajamas out. Please, Vince, help him undress—if he needs it."

Vince nods and I go into the small bedroom which Owen will now be sharing with his younger brother. Tim is sound asleep. I turn down the top sheet and place Owen's pajamas neatly on top of the pillow . . . *HANG TOUGH—BUT BE MELLOW.* . . . His message strengthens me.

"Owen," I urge, "it's late and you've had a long trip home. Why don't you get some sleep now?"

Owen shakes his head.

"C'mon, now," Vince says, gently, "we're all tired. Let's all get some sleep. Okay?"

Owen rocks more insistently. Vince goes over and, helping him up to his feet, walks him into his bedroom.

Relieved, I put out the lights and retire to my room. Vince comes in and asks me to say good-night to Owen.

I enter the darkened room. The hall light has been left on and it shines into the room. Owen is stretched out, stiffly, above the covers, face up. His eyes are wide open, gleaming brightly up at the ceiling.

Bending softly over him, I kiss him on the forehead. "Goodnight, Owen. Please get some sleep now. Here, let me help you under the covers."

I tuck him in, glance nervously at the sleeping Timothy, and close the door gently behind me.

Midnight. The witching hour. It is quiet now. Yet I cannot sleep. A feeling of nameless dread pervades the atmosphere. Like Owen I cannot move, but must lie, mummylike, on my back staring blankly at the dim ceiling. Waiting. Knowing he is out there. Thinking strange thoughts. Acting like one possessed.

Suddenly Vince sits upright. He bolts out the door.

I get up slowly. Not wanting to get up. Yet knowing how foolish we were to have tried to go to sleep.

I find Vincent walking down the hall with his arm around Owen.

"What happened?" I ask. It is nearly 1 A.M.

"He was in the kitchen, making a phone call."

"At this hour? To whom?"

"I don't know," Vince replies. "He muttered a name I never heard of."

Owen smiles. Eyes glimmering.

"What will we do?" I ask. "He can't walk around like this all night making mysterious phone calls."

"I know, I know. I tried getting him back into bed, but he just got right out again. I've never seen him like this. He's so restless; it's incredible." Vince walks Owen into the living room and sits down on the sofa beside him.

I sit in the rocker now and begin to rock, staring at the strange young man in our midst. "Yes, I've never seen him like this, either. But it isn't Owen before us. It isn't Owen."

"Now *you're* not making any sense, Ursula."

"I'm making sense, all right. This is not Owen—not as we know him. But I'm too tired and it's too late to dispute this point. We must get him to bed. He simply can't disrupt the whole family. We've all been through enough for one day."

"How do you suggest I get him to go to sleep? Tie him down to the bed?"

"No, of course not. You'll just have to sleep next to him, Vince, just for tonight." I remember the psychiatrist, hoping that he will give him strong sleeping pills, if nothing else.

"You're right," Vince says, totally unconvinced. "C'mon, Owen, we're sleeping here in the living room tonight."

We walk Owen over to the daybed in the living room and get him into it, next to the wall. Vince lies down beside him, arm protectively on his shoulder, and I turn off the light.

I return to my bedroom and check the time.

It is now one o'clock in the morning.

The long nightmare has begun.

3

ABSURD NEW WORLD

Monday morning. Another bright blue autumn sky. Another golden sun. Vincent wakes me with a kiss. Like Sleeping Beauty I gently stir awake.

"You're going to need all the encouragement you can get," he says. "It won't be an easy day for you. He's up and he's not making any sense at all."

I stretch lazily and get out of bed. It is very quiet and peaceful. The other children have already left for school. Vincent has just left for work.

We are now alone, Owen and I.

He is in his bedroom, seated on the edge of his bed. Eyebrows knotted. Blank eyes in a Mephistophelean stare. I chide myself for thinking such thoughts and force a smile.

"Come on into my room," I suggest. "I'll bring you breakfast in bed."

To my surprise, Owen readily accepts the suggestion.

I turn on the stereo in my bedroom and put his favorite Beatles record on, "Hey Jude." He seems pleased as I fuss over him, fluffing two pillows behind his head and setting the breakfast tray on his lap.

"I made you pancakes. You always liked them."

"Coffee. Bring more coffee," he commands.

I return with the coffee pot and refill his cup.

"Paper," he demands. "I have to have paper. I have to write, Mother. Don't you understand? I have to write."

I bring in a legal pad and a pen. He pushes the breakfast away, half-finished, and begins to write, furiously.

As I lean over, trying to see his work, he pats the bed next to him. "Here, Mother, come here."

Shocked, I step back. "No," I say, firmly, "I must do the dishes now."

"Bring more coffee," he commands.

I come back in with the pot and refill his cup as he continues, totally absorbed in his writing.

Mathematical calculations fill the pages:

$$
\begin{array}{rl}
24 & \\
+24 & \quad 1 \\
\hline
48 & \\
+24 & \quad 2 \\
\hline
72 & \\
+24 & \quad 3 \\
\hline
96 & \\
+24 & \quad 4 \\
\hline
120 & \\
+24 & \quad 5 \\
\hline
144 & \\
+24 & \quad 6 \\
\hline
168 & \\
+24 & \quad 7 \\
\hline
192 & \\
+24 & \quad 8 \\
\hline
216 & \\
+24 & \quad 9 \\
\hline
240 &
\end{array}
$$

$$+24 \quad 10$$
$$\overline{(264)}$$
$$+24 \quad 11$$
$$\overline{(288)}$$
$$+24 \quad 12$$
$$\overline{(312)}$$
$$+24 \quad 13$$
$$\overline{(336)}$$
$$+24 \quad 14$$
$$\overline{(360)}$$
$$15$$

I marvel at the mathematical symmetry of it all. Picking up his discarded sheets of paper through the morning I study them. For clues. To what?

$$TUV = 8$$
$$58 = 0$$
$$25 = 1$$
$$51 = 9$$
$$95 = \text{Alphabet}$$
$$GOD = \text{me I can see}$$
POWER

And he talks. Incessantly. All through the long day he rambles on, incoherently, only occasionally making sense. He points to our new Siamese kitten. "The eyes, Mother. Check out the eyes." They gleam. Like his own.

All is abstract. The world of reality has suddenly been replaced by a strange, absurd new world of symbols, terse, repetitive symbols. Owen's genius for math has always been in evidence—he even excelled in calculus—and I try, bravely, to communicate with him through these same symbols. He is pleased that I "understand."

All day the legal pad fills up. He continues to write letters, equations. Strange sentences and symbols appear:

Religion is key

R-P (Rel-P)

Ⓘ

Ⓚey to the Future

← G.G.G.G.G. →

W.W.

G.P.

General

Practitioner

← C.C.C. →

Bio

Feedback

Revelation

J.C.

C. Ⓒ C.

Cancer

J.C. (Jesus, J.C.)

has *cancer*

It *does* have meaning! It all has meaning. He is obsessed with religion. As a Jew he is concerned for the safety of the Jews (he had been reading a book on Jewish history at the university while taking a course on the subject) and he now fears for Jesus Christ (a Jew). Jesus has cancer. Yes, I understand. I see what he is trying to say. But why must it all be in symbols, in equations? And why doesn't the frenzied writing stop?

It is now lunchtime. I look for Owen. He is nowhere in sight. Frantically I search the five-room apartment. Finally, I notice that the master bathroom door is closed. I turn the knob. Locked! "Owen?" I call. No answer. "Owen—I know you're in there.

Please . . . please come out! It's lunchtime." No response. I think of the super but immediately reject that idea. Thinking clearly once more, I rummage through my handbag, feeling around for my keys. Success! I find the thin emergency key and insert it in the lock. Cautiously I open the door. Inside I find Owen seated on the lid of the toilet seat, the legal pad on his lap, writing. "Love thyself, love thyself," he is mumbling.

"Owen," I implore, relieved that he is all right, "please come for lunch. I've made you an omelet."

"Shush—" he puts his index finger to his lips. "Shush."

He continues the frenetic writing.

I go over and pull him to his feet. "You can write later. I have a nice hot lunch for you. Come." He won't release the pad as we walk into the dining room together.

"Generations, mother," he tells me excitedly at lunch. "Every twenty-five years. Generations." I nod in agreement. He refuses to eat. He is more agitated than before. He grabs the legal pad once more and writes:

J.L. will be

Ⓟ rez

of Ⓤ Ⓢ

too Ⓢ Ⓜ Ⓐ Ⓡ Ⓣ

Ⓖramps

㉕

inspiration

balanced?

10

25 generation

tech-

nocracy

Owen runs out of paper. Not to be discouraged, he snatches the calendar off my desk and begins to cover it with symbols, circling the numbers in each month, writing a series of abstruse equations:

$$Jews = 3 = 4 = Physics$$
bring the calendar Quick
$$Q\ Q\ Q\ Q$$
$$LAS\ Q\ Q\ Q\ Q\ 4\ hearts$$
$$LAS\ Q\ Q\ Q\ Q\ 4\ hearts\ M.S.C.$$
$$H.M.S.C.$$
$$H.M.S.C.$$
$$1 = guilt$$
$$2 = shades$$
$$1 = duty$$

The calendar has now become the medium for his message. I am completely fascinated by this copious verbal and written outpouring. Charmed by it. I find myself helplessly sucked into the maelstrom of his madness, carried away by the currents of his strange thought processes, mesmerized by this master "of the symbol and the metaphor," as psychiatrist Arthur Burton describes persons like Owen. Owen now "holds the figurative key to life" having "the deepest insights into the human condition which comes to others with only the greatest difficulty or never at all."

I am morbidly enchanted by it all, and later am to turn to yet another psychiatrist, Morton Schatzman, who declares in his book, *Soul Murder*, that "mental illness may eventually belong to the domain, not of physicians, but of linguists and communications analysts."

The eyes of my inspired soliloquist gleam in revelation as he rambles on and on, with the greatest facility, his mind altered, mysteriously expanded. The wonder of it all overwhelms me as I watch and listen in speechless fascination.

The calendar is now effectively demolished. Undaunted, he takes to the Sunday *Times* magazine section for his next source of paper, scribbling on the crossword puzzle page, significantly titled "Freudian Flips":

We know too much

SEX

GUILT

(ME)

JESUS = G.O.D.

He tosses the *Times* away and grabs the latest issue of *Time* magazine. He scrawls, meaningfully, across a page:

COME TOGETHER MAD

Owen stops writing. He has written himself out.

But the agitation worsens.

When Suzy and Tim come home from school Owen is pacing rapidly back and forth, ranting loudly, "Guilt." The word has been announced all afternoon. He is severely agitated. Disoriented.

Violence erupts. He grabs his twelve-year-old brother and for no apparent reason begins to punch him, furiously, on the shoulder. Horrified, I pull the younger boy away.

"Stop it, Owen!"

He now grabs my wrist and squeezes very hard.

"I'm going to kill you, Mother!" he warns.

I am unable to move, his grasp is so strong.

Finally he releases me.

I rush over to the children. "I want you both to go over to Mrs. Morgan's. Tell her you have to use her phone—and don't give any explanations. Just go!"

"Who do you want us to call?" asks Suzy.

"I want you to call Howard. It's after four, he should be home from his school now."

"What should I tell him?"

"Tell him that Owen is . . . very sick and that I need him. Now!"

I watch Tim and Suzy go down the stairs and out to safety.

I am glad that I thought of Howard. He is so big and strong, yet so compassionate; a true friend.

Owen is momentarily quiet. He is seated on the rocking chair in the living room.

I go over to the wall phone in the kitchen, where I can easily see the living room, and try Howard's number. No answer.

There is nothing else I can do but stand in the kitchen doorway and observe Owen. What if he walks menacingly toward me? Then I will have to call the police. The thought of doing that is utterly repugnant. But what else am I to do? Am I safe? Whom do I turn to?

I must keep my distance. Owen's violence now seems triggered by close contact with anyone. Seated at the dining room table, facing the living room, I thumb through the newspaper. I cannot concentrate. But I must keep my cool. I must wait it out.

Finally, at five o'clock, I hear the key in the lock.

Vincent, my Prince Charming of the morning, has returned home early. A first for him. I have never been so happy to see him. The children follow him, cautiously, up the stairs. They have told him what to expect.

"Let's grab a bite to eat, Ursula, and get him over to that psychiatrist."

We eat, but Owen refuses to join us.

"Come, Owen," I coax, "we are going out for a drive." I help him on with his jacket. He is more subdued now. He is probably tired; it has been an ordeal—for all of us. Fortunately, the psychiatrist is only two miles from our home. In the car Owen sits quietly between Tim and me. We do not trust him next to the door.

I breathe a sigh of relief when we find the waiting room empty. Owen stretches out on the carpeted floor, hands behind his head. He is exhausted.

The doctor greets us soon after we arrive. He glances momentarily at Owen and asks Vincent and me to come in first.

I describe my day in detail: Owen's bizarre behavior, his incoherent speech patterns, the unexpected violence. All events are recounted as matter-of-factly as possible.

"There must be an explanation, doctor!" I blurt out.

"Yes, of course. But first let me see your son. If you will both wait outside I will talk to him now."

Vince gets Owen up and walks him to the inner office.

After fifteen minutes the doctor calls us both back inside.

"I'm surprised you didn't bring him to me sooner."

"But, doctor," I remind him, "you said you couldn't see him any sooner."

"Did I?"

He had forgotten.

"What can you tell us?" Vince asks.

"That your son needs hospitalization—and as soon as possible."

"You mean tonight?" I ask.

"Tonight."

"Where do we take him?"

"The Long Island Medical Center is probably the best place. It's certainly the closest. Let me give the psych emergency room a call."

The psychiatrist is told to send us right down.

"Shall I go back for his clothes?" I ask. "I didn't even bring his pajamas."

"No, Mrs. Etons," he warns. "You cannot waste a moment. Get him over to the hospital directly."

We get Owen back into the car and I tell him we are going to take him to a place that will help him get better. He is silent now. It is almost as if he knows where he is going, as if he knows that he is ill.

No one speaks during the ten-mile ride to the medical center. It is a sad journey for all of us. But it is one we must make. We must make Owen well again.

4

PSYCH E-R

The Long Island Medical Center is the tallest building in Marsey County. Fifteen stories high, it dominates the rustic suburban landscape. It is a symbol of contemporary, dignified power. The red rooftop lights blink for miles, warning low-flying planes, but for me they are a welcoming signal.

We enter the lower level of the medical center. The psychiatric emergency room, or Psych E-R as it is called, is located at the far end of a long hallway, past the medical E-R.

Locked double doors greet us. There is no visible bell so I knock, repeatedly. A nurse inside finally responds and lets us in.

"Who's the patient?" she demands.

I point to Owen.

"Okay, but they'll [she points to Suzy and Tim] have to wait outside."

The children leave and the nurse bolts the double doors behind us.

"Is there a doctor on duty?" I ask, naively.

"There's *always* a doctor on duty here," she informs me. "You'll have to wait your turn."

The Psych E-R is, literally, a lower level of hell. We must wait. And wait. And wait.

Owen paces the long corridor. Back and forth. Back and forth.

He wanders behind the reception counter into the nurses' station and starts playing with what appear to be pneumatic tubes of some sort. The nurse admonishes him and escorts him out. He smiles and mumbles incoherently. I sit him down beside me, but in a minute he is up again, pacing. His restlessness astounds me, for I am now very tired. It is ten o'clock at night.

Vincent goes out to check the younger children. I glance at another person, waiting for admission. She is a married woman, about thirty, whose husband stands beside her. She is seated on a chair and is methodically pulling off her shoes, one at a time. She wears no stockings. Her husband tries to put them back on but she pushes him away. She is now, happily, barefooted. Her husband shakes his head and sits down nearby.

Owen comes back and sits down beside me. Within five seconds he is up again.

Vincent returns. He puts his arm around Owen's shoulder and walks up and down the long corridor with him.

There appears to be only one doctor on duty and he is in the office with a patient. Two other people besides Owen are waiting to be admitted: the barefoot woman and a young woman, seated next to her older sister, crying softly.

Vince shakes his head sadly as he walks back to me, his arm still around Owen's shoulder. "We never should have brought the kids. They have homework and now they're stuck here for the night. I think I ought to take them home and come back for you."

"No," I answer quickly. "You're not leaving me now. I want you here to speak to the doctor with me."

At that moment we hear a key turn noisily in the bolted double door and as if in answer to my prayers another doctor comes walking briskly in. He is bespeckled, thirtyish, and seems pleasant and confident. He nods to the nurse and proceeds into the other examining room.

"Now we should be seen very shortly," I assure Vincent. He and Owen sit down beside me.

Finally, Owen is called in by the psychiatrist who has just arrived.

It is 10:30 P.M.

The interview lasts approximately a half hour. I am pleased because it seems to me that we will get an accurate diagnosis. The doctor asks Owen to wait in the corridor and Vincent and I are called in.

I tearfully hand the psychiatrist sheets of Owen's unorthodox writings; I have a plethora of them. The doctor smiles, his eyes are kind, and hands them back to me, keeping only one sheet.

"You must tell me what is wrong," I plead. "He came home from college like this yesterday. It's all so sudden! Why, he's never been like this before. He's always been so good, so bright —so well adjusted. Why, he's just—always been an angel."

"Yes, I'm sure," the doctor replies softly.

"And now, for no reason at all, he's like this. He reminds me of the schizophrenics I read about in abnormal psych in college— but he couldn't be! He's never had an emotional problem in his life!"

"I know," the doctor replies. "From what I can ascertain, it appears to be a drug-induced psychosis."

"Drug-induced," Vince repeats.

"It's too early to make a definitive diagnosis, but from speaking to your son and from observing his behavior, that is my tentative diagnosis."

"He's been smoking marijuana," I inform the psychiatrist.

"Not surprising," he replies.

"And he might have been on speed, too."

"I see." He makes some notes.

"What will they be able to do for him?" Vince asks.

"He'll get the necessary medication—and therapy," the doctor states.

"Can you be more specific?" I ask.

"All drug-induced psychoses are treated like schizophrenia. You mentioned how his speech and behavior reminded you of your readings on the subject. Well, that's just how we go about treating a case like this. As to medication, he will be given one of the major tranquilizers, which one I don't know. That will be up to the doctor in charge of his case. In fact, they probably won't give him anything at all at first. They'll want to find out what he's been taking, if they can."

"You mean they'll leave him alone—like *this?*" I cannot hide my concern.

"They'll do what's best for him at the moment," the doctor assures me. "Now, in a few minutes we will ask him to sign the commitment papers. He's just turned nineteen, am I correct?"

"Yes," I reply. "He was just nineteen this month."

"I don't think we will have any problem getting him to sign. And then they will escort him to Ward Ten."

"What is Ward Ten?" Vincent asks.

"Ten is our locked ward."

"A locked ward?" I asked, fearfully.

The psychiatrist replies firmly. "It is the best place for him at this time. For his own safety and for the safety of others I must assign him there." He softens. "Later on, when he is well enough, they will transfer him to the new building, up to the open ward."

The interview is ended. Vincent and I shake hands with the doctor and go out once more into the corridor to wait with Owen.

In a few minutes Owen is called to the nurses' station. The doctor readies the commitment papers and presents them to him. He signs, readily.

Then he is beside us once more. And again we wait. And wait. And wait.

Owen is very sleepy. He wanders into one of the little cubicles off the corridor and lies down on a hospital bed.

I approach the nurse. "It's after eleven; we've been here for hours. When will he be going to the ward? He's exhausted."

"He'll have to wait for security."

"Security?"

"That's right. And the shift is changing now, so it'll be a little while longer."

Armed guards disturb me. What will Owen's reaction be?

I say nothing but sit down beside Vincent. We are both too tired to talk.

Soft sobbing startles me. I turn to see the young, thin woman, soon to be parted from her sister. Two nurses are conversing, the shift is changing over, and they say she is suicidal. The open ward, upstairs, refuses to take her. She, too, must be sent to the locked ward.

Her sobbing intensifies. I am crying, too. Inside.

I go into the cubicle to check on Owen. He is stretched out, eyes wide open, immobile. Staring blankly at the ceiling. I kiss him lightly on the forehead and stroke his thick blond hair.

"It's okay. It's okay. You'll stay here for awhile—and then you'll be just fine."

Owen says nothing.

"I will come every day. I promise. I promise."

He says nothing.

I go back into the corridor.

"It's eleven-thirty," I protest, this time to a different nurse. "We've been here for hours—"

"I know. I'm calling Ten again. They should be down for him soon."

Finally, after more than four long hours in Psych E-R, two armed, uniformed security guards arrive to escort my son to Ward 10.

It is midnight.

I go in to tell Owen that they are going to bring him to a nice, quiet place where he can get some rest. Where he can get well again. He gets up immediately.

Another nurse has arrived. She will also accompany him to the ward. I am glad, because her presence softens the harshness of the guards.

Vince pats him gently on the back. "Take care, Son."

I hug him tightly and kiss him on the cheek. "I love you, Owen. I love you very, very much."

I know he understands.

Then we stand silently by as he, my young, gentle college boy, is led away by two burly uniformed guards to a strange, secret place.

5

OWEN

Light peeks from behind the hill
To shine upon expectant ones;
Clears visions disfigured in darkness
and roosts upon the sleepy.
The sky speckled in white
becomes blend to early morning viewers,
and a tranquilizer to men of other times.
Calendars and numbered watches
reveal a new day
without prophecy to tell of what comes.

"Sunrise"—this is how Owen had seen it and felt it and written about it. This poem of his was published in an anthology of students' works.

But now—now the poems have changed.

Turn it on and off but
not with the door open spec-
tators see what
the cut did to you theres
a cut over my eye and its
killing my brain

I want to know what's killing his brain. I call the university and speak to his roommate, Greg.

"You must tell me what happened," I plead.

"I really don't know."

"You must know something."

"I don't know what to tell you—"

"There must have been signs that something was wrong."

"Well, he did start acting strange. He started doing funny things."

"What do you mean?"

"Well, his whole personality changed. At first, he was just short-tempered. Then he began arguing a lot."

"About what?"

"Strange things. He argued in symbols."

"What else?"

"He started running through the dorm halls, ripping things down."

"What things?"

"You know, notes and stuff that people put up on their doors."

"What else can you tell me that was unusual?"

"He began cutting classes."

"That's not at all like Owen."

"Yeah, I know."

"For how long was he cutting classes?"

"Oh, I'd say for at least two weeks."

"How was he just before this happened . . . just before he was sent home?"

"We went to a party the night before, you know, Saturday night, and he was . . . well, he was freaked out. It was obvious."

"Is there anything else you can tell me?"

"Well, he hadn't slept in four nights."

"Four nights!"

"That's right."

"What about pot? You can tell me."

"There's nothing to tell. He smoked it. Lots of it. He smoked every night."

"Every night?"

"Every night."

"And what else did he take?"

"Gosh, Mrs. Etons, I really don't know."

"Was he on speed?"

"Could've been."

"Greg, I want you to help me—to help Owen. If you find anything else out, please call me. Call me collect."

"Okay. If I find out anything more."

I return to his recent poem, and read on.

> it makes me nervous but im better now; you
> can get worse, you know theres theres always to-
> morrow tomorrow to-morrow theres always to-
> morrow to-morrow to-

Scraps of paper fall, like large crumpled snowflakes, from his notebook. On each is scrawled a poem. The handwriting has disintegrated.

> It's dinnertime but I'm not hungry
> it's just the clock on the wall
> which triggers a clock in my tummy
> books can nourish me
> smoke can nourish me

Owen . . . nine pounds two ounces of beautiful baby boy. "He's the biggest newborn in the nursery," I tell Vincent, beaming proudly.

For months I nurse him and he thrives. At two he is so gloriously beautiful that I cannot stop photographing him. Pale blond curls, bright blue eyes, an enchanting smile.

But under that angelic smile, an imp lurks. For, while very little, in company with his baby sister (twenty months his junior), Owen seeks out danger. A lit lamp wire is cut, out of curiosity, and he is almost killed. Then, on another occasion, an electrical display mysteriously begins to smoke in the window of my favorite, posh beauty parlor.

Owen remembers his mischievous deeds. At age thirteen he writes his autobiography:

I was born at an early age, or so my mother used to tell me. I learned to walk at 11 months, learned to talk at 15 months, and learned how to burn down beauty parlors at 18 months. This tremendous skill stayed with me until I realized that it wasn't a very

good way of attracting attention, because every time I did it, the insurance man would get mad at my mother, and my mother would tell my father, and I wouldn't be able to sit down for 2 weeks. However, I found it quite simple to adapt to other trades. One such trade was cutting lamp cords with a gigantic scissor, which I called a "chicken scissor" because I was always chicken to use it. When I got bored with these trades, I would turn to other things as sources of enjoyment. One such thing was the sidewalk. One day, while my mother was preoccupied with my booby-baby sister, I took a walk—a long, long walk. And since I was only 2½, it seemed even longer. When my mother realized I was gone, she became frantic and called the police. After a while, I began to feel lost, which I was, so I turned back for home. At this point, the police decided it was hopeless, so my mother continued the search herself. Four hours had passed when I realized I had taken a walk around the block.

Such perilous experiences left me windless and exhausted. Because of this, I set aside 1 hour each day for a nap. I came to call this "The Daily Nap" which sounded more like a newspaper, than what it was. After a few days, two, to be exact, I quit and subjected myself to ridicule from my mother. She would say things as: "Owen, pull down your pants so I can smack you in the face." It was orders like this that put me one step closer to insubordination.

But insubordination is never a problem at school. Owen excels in every academic area. At junior high he is placed in Honors English and Math and does remarkably well. The teachers all adore this happy, enthusiastic boy. He participates in all class discussions and enjoys the academic life.

Creativity is, however, the most striking aspect of Owen's personality. He paints beautiful landscapes in oil, most of them done during the ages of thirteen and fourteen. He sketches famous people. He plays the piano and takes up the clarinet in school. And he sings, is accepted into the high school choir, and performs in all of the special concerts.

But his poems are his most impressive creations. He writes voluminously and is encouraged by one of his English teachers.

He continues to write poetry in his first year of college. Whimsical poems abound and they are not for publication, only for enjoyment.

The pleasantries of last year's poems have turned to despair.

One of his latest works (they are dated) is entitled "To Be a Poet":

> to be a poet
>   "this guy is sick"
> to be a poet
>   "he's *really* sick"
> look at his writing its
>   covered with words
> look at it, look at it,
>   how ABSURD!
> what a waste, what a waste,
>   how could he waste his time so?
> it doesn't much matter
>   he won't make a dime so
> what does it matter, i mean
>   if he dies
> will it sadden the world?
>   will it darken the skies?

When were the skies their brightest? My mind turns back. . . . We are seated at the high school Honors Award ceremony. I present Vincent with a letter I have just received from Owen's French teacher:

It is with a great deal of pleasure that I write to you about your son, Owen.

Throughout the year, he was an outstanding student—in both achievement and attitude. For this, he merits special commendation.

Owen is presented with four awards at the Honors ceremony. He is also the recipient of a Regents Scholarship.

We are so proud. So proud. . . .

What has happened, Owen? Where has the sparkle gone? Why has the hope faded, like dry winter grass? . . .

> My heart is dead, sincerely
> I felt it this morning in the woods when god called
> I thought I saw it
> but I could be mistaken.
> One never knows
> one never really knows

God come back to me
you are my only lover
I am sorry
I am hurt
keep me covered

I weep for my hurt child.

6

WALK OF THE ZOMBIES

It is hidden away, like some dark malignant growth, on the first floor of the old part of the medical center. For it is, after all, a locked psychiatric ward, one that houses the most violent patients.

I approach Ward 10 with caution. The door is tightly bolted. A sign is posted, with instructions. I ring the bell. A voice responds from within.

"Who is it?"

"It's Mrs. Etons. I'd like to see my son Owen."

"You'll have to wait. We open in five minutes." The intercom snaps off.

I study the sign. It states that visiting is limited to one hour a day from 1:00 to 2:00 P.M. on Tuesday, Thursday, and Saturday and from 7:00 to 8:00 P.M. on Monday, Wednesday, Friday, and Sunday.

Two other people have now come into the corridor. They sit down on a hard wooden bench. I am too restless to sit. I put down my shopping bag, containing some personal things for Owen, and stand by the door.

Five minutes go by. Then ten. I knock on the door. There is a rustling sound from within. The door opens noisily.

I am greeted by a heavy-set woman, obviously the receptionist. She is accompanied by a uniformed guard.

"Come in," she orders, impatiently.

I walk over to the reception desk and sign in.

"What's in the shopping bag?" she demands. I hand the shopping bag to her.

"It's only some clothes—he has no pajamas. And, oh yes, I brought him a malted. He hasn't been eating—"

"Okay, okay, but we have to check it every time you come. And remember, no matches."

"No, I won't bring him any matches." I take back my shopping bag.

"Now, if you'll have a seat, they'll send him out in a minute."

I scrutinize the dingy room. Three black vinyl sofas, a couple of hard chairs, one large window, facing north, an obscure view of the back service lot. It is quite cold in the room. A tall radiator stands under the window. I touch it. It is ice cold.

A neatly uniformed nurse approaches me. "Mrs. Etons, we don't usually do this, but your son is not able to come out to the visiting room. You'll have to come into his room to see him. But we can't let you stay too long. It's his first day."

"Is he getting any medication?"

"No. Not yet."

"Who is his doctor? I'd like to speak with him."

"I don't know. I'll have to check the records. Please come with me."

I follow her inside and down a long, narrow corridor. She admits me into a small room. Owen is standing, garbed in a hospital gown. His eyes gleam in recognition as I approach.

"Hi, Owen. I brought you a chocolate malted." I hand him the large container. He drinks quickly and then looks hard at me.

"Dad is dead," he states.

All verbal inhibitions have failed. Freud had warned us: "It is the fate of all of us . . . to direct our first sexual impulse towards our mother and our first hatred and our first murderous wish against our father."

"Dad is fine," I assure him. "Dad is alive."

"No, Dad is dead," he insists. "Kennedy is alive."

"Owen," I change the subject, "I want to know what you've been taking. Did you take any drugs?"

His glassy eyes brighten. "I took two black pills, Mother. It was LSD."

I believe him, and inwardly shudder to think of the damage it might do to his brain.

The nurse interrupts. "Time to go, Mrs. Etons."

"Here, Owen, I brought you a change of clothes and some pajamas."

"Here, I'll take those," the nurse says. "We have to keep everything in a special closet."

"What about his glasses?" I ask. "He hasn't worn them since he got back from school, and he does need them. He's near-sighted."

"No glasses," she says, firmly.

I kiss Owen very lightly on the cheek. "Good-bye, dear. I'll see you tomorrow."

The nurse leads me over to her station.

"His doctor's name is Sand. He was seen this morning by Dr. Sand and the chief psychiatrist, Dr. Ressler. Here is Dr. Sand's number if you wish to phone him tomorrow. He's in Neurology."

"Neurology?"

"Yes."

I take the phone number from her. This is most interesting, and I must discuss it with Vincent.

That evening I bring up the subject. "Owen's doctor is a neurologist. What do you think of that?"

"Well," he informs me, "Freud's medical degree was in psychiatry-neurology."

"Yes," I now recall, "the two fields are interrelated. In fact, I would much rather have a neurologist on the case than a psychiatrist. Neurologists may have more practical medical knowledge. Psychiatrists appear to be too theoretical."

"Listen, I don't care what kind of degree the guy has as long as he gets Owen well."

It is Wednesday morning and I call Dr. Sand.

"We'll be starting him on medication tomorrow," he assures

me. "We had to give whatever was in his system a chance to get out."

"What medication will you be giving him?"

"Well, we have a choice of two antipsychotic drugs, or major tranquilizers as they are popularly called. We can use either Thorazine or haloperidol. I've decided to use the haloperidol—Haldol is its brand name—because it's much faster acting."

Haldol. The name has a magical quality to it. It is a super-drug, I discover, which inhibits the action of dopamine, a chemical in the brain, and corrects the imbalance of nerve impulse transmissions. But Haldol can have a devastating effect on the rest of the body—as I am soon to find out.

"Good!" I innocently remark. "I can't wait for him to start."

"Remember, Mrs. Etons," he cautions, "you won't see any improvement for a while. It takes a week to ten days for the drug to clear up the present chemical imbalance in his brain."

"Doctor, do you know what he's been taking?"

"Well, we know he's been taking marijuana, and quite a bit of it, but there's something else—possibly speed, but probably something more potent."

"Could it be LSD?"

"I don't know. Frankly, I doubt it. But don't worry, we'll find out soon enough."

I rejoice when medication begins on Wednesday. Owen receives the Haldol, by injection at first, three times a day—a total of thirty milligrams. It makes him very, very groggy.

For the first couple of days, Owen seems to get worse. The overt agitation has ceased, but he is now in a somnambulistic state. He sits, eyes closed, in the visitors' room. He will not, cannot, communicate. And when he walks, he does not walk at all; he glides—very stiffly. For he has become one of *them*. Owen has become a zombie.

I call it the March of the Zombies. The scene is the waiting room. The visitors always sit, silent and still, as the patients come out. One by one these zombies slide out, stiffly, clad only in hospital white, ghostly white, eyes staring blankly ahead, sliding slowly, then stopping when rescued by a waiting relative. It is an eerie scene. And it never changes.

Owen now belongs to *their* world. A strange, four-dimensional world. No communication. No recognition.

He sits with me today, eyes closed. I have just brought him a hamburger from McDonald's. He is obviously unable to feed himself and I want to help.

"How are you feeling?" I touch his shoulder gently.

"Get out of here!" He angrily brushes me away. Eyes still closed.

"I've brought you a hamburger from McDonald's. Will you have a bite?"

No response.

Somewhat embarrassed, I glance at the other visitors.

Silence.

I take a brush from my handbag and lightly brush his tangled hair. I notice that he is shaking slightly.

Before I leave, I question the nurse.

"It's the side effects of the medication," she tells me.

"And the stiffness, the tilting forward when he walks?"

"The medication," she repeats.

I glance around at the others. So these zombies are not really zombies after all. They are, probably, the physical end result of overmedication.

Several days pass. Days of silence, of irrationality; and yet, I gradually see some improvement. Owen asks for his glasses (request denied). And he is calmer now. The Haldol is surging through his system.

The ward population is youthful. I get to know some of the other patients: the young man, my son's age, who's been in and out of the hospital and who laughs, psychopathically, all of the time, and the young woman, age twenty-four, who is silent all of the time. She is depressed. This is also a return visit for her. I commiserate with their mothers. It sustains me.

Every day I visit with Owen for the one appointed hour. I now bring him malteds from the hospital coffee shop; they are easier to force-feed than hamburgers. He drinks them because he is thirsty. Another result of the medication.

And although it is November I talk to him of the spring.

"Look!" I present him with a large, glossy book on vegetable gardening. He has always enjoyed growing his own vegetables, so now I talk of his gardening, past and future.

"Remember that large garden you once had? And all those cucumbers! Remember? We had to give them away to all the neighbors." I smile at that sea of cucumbers.

"Now, as soon as you're better, we're going to look for another house. We'll be in it by this spring or summer and you'll have a vegetable garden again. Look . . . look at these lovely pictures." I turn the pages for him.

By the weekend, Owen asks to go home. I tell him we will speak to the doctor. He remembers the name of his doctor.

On Sunday he is silent. Morose. I try to cheer him up.

"Tomorrow is Halloween. Would you like me to bring you some candy?"

"I'd love it," he responds. I am heartened.

It is now Monday—Halloween—one week since Owen has been hospitalized. But he has only been on medication for five days.

Dr. Sand calls me with encouraging information.

"Good news," he says, cheerily. "Owen seems better, more oriented." He goes on to say that he expects to have him transferred up to O-P, the open ward.

We visit Owen in the evening and tell him the good news. He is uncheered. Sullen. I notice that his hands are held in a strange, puppy-dog position. They are stiff. His body shakes slightly. "I'm very nervous," he explains.

"No, you're not. It's just the medication. You're much, much better. And just think, soon you'll be in the new wing of the hospital."

He seems concerned. Not at all happy with the prospect. Fatigue overtakes him. He leans against Vincent's shoulder and dozes off.

On Tuesday I question Dr. Sand. What, I want to know, has triggered this psychosis? What culprit drug?

"Well, as you know, he's been on heavy quantities of marijuana—that alone can cause problems—and he's even taken speed. But the thing that really blew his mind was angel dust."

Angel dust. So that was it!

Angel dust. The deadly drug I had read about in all the newspapers and magazines.

I must find out more. I am determined to investigate the subject.

I visit Owen in the afternoon. I take one look and I know he is on the mend. He still walks stiffly, with his body tilted forward, but he is clean, combed, and wide awake. And he is articulate once more. His mood is pleasant.

"I'd like to get out of here," he tells me. "I need some fresh air."

I don't blame him. Ward 10 is dingy and depressing. The worst possible setting for a mentally ill person.

"You'll be out of here soon, Owen. Very, very soon."

It is to be his last day in 10.

For now. . . .

7

OF POT AND PEACE PILLS

The Absurd World versus the Real World. Mental illness versus mental health. Pot versus the PeaCe Pill. I ponder these problems. Owen is in the hospital now. Why?

Owen.

In September a bright, articulate, charming, functional eighteen-year-old.

In October a dazed, irrational, violent, nonfunctional nineteen-year-old.

In one month a metamorphosis has taken place. Why?

Dr. Arthur Burton has made some interesting observations. The following quotations are from his book, *The Alchemy of Schizophrenia:*

"Adolescence is the crisis time of life when a *life plan* is effectuated and a life style demanded for work, love, and procreation" and "One of the surprising findings of the use of mind-expanding drugs has been how quickly and easily one can become schizophrenic—give up the basic parameter of reality and reason."

And what about the effect of these drugs? Dr. Burton continues: "Chemistry is pernicious . . . the effect is to dull the total participation of the person in anything meaningful in life and to maintain withdrawal as a reserve."

Psychiatrists have now become philosophers. Burton goes on to state that society contributes to mental illness: "An unbearable nuclear and distal metapsychological milieu is the basis of schizophrenia."

And what of the symptoms of schizophrenia, which these drug-induced psychoses such as Owen's resemble—what of them?

Schizophrenia is a "peculiar form of self-punishment [*guilt, mother, guilt*] . . . the schizophrenic takes the suffering upon himself and releases his family and society from obligation."

Dr. Burton continues, philosophically, to discuss schizophrenia —and drug-induced psychoses—as "a person's highly unique response to a world full of paradoxes and Absurdities he cannot accept or live with. . . . The so-called thinking disorder of the schizophrenic is not a disorder at all. It is the patient's way of communication with a world he no longer wants to be part of; it is his way of highlighting the Absurdity he finds around him."

Another psychiatrist, Werner M. Mendel, also writes in this vein. In his book, *A Phenomenological Theory of Schizophrenia,* he asks the following questions: "Does one have the right to impose consensually validated reality on idiosyneratic reality? . . . Is it philosophically justified to treat someone or to intervene in his life because he doesn't fit into the life style of the majority culture or the majority culture calls him sick?"

This is exactly what the British psychiatrist R. D. Laing has expressed in his writings. In the preface to *The Divided Self* he writes:

A little girl of seventeen in a mental hospital told me she was terrified because the Atom Bomb was inside her. That is a delusion. The statesmen of the world who boast and threaten that they have Doomsday weapons are far more dangerous, and far more estranged from 'reality' than many of the people on whom the label 'psychotic' is affixed.

It seems as if our Absurd New World is not so absurd, after all. It can often be more mathematically symmetrical, more musically sonorous, more perfectly poetical, than a Real World in which a United States congressman is shot dead while visiting his constituents in a foreign country, causing a "religious" leader to exhort his followers to their mass suicides. Almost one thousand perish, voluntarily, in this Real World.

The world of schizophrenia and drug-induced psychoses is oftentimes more pleasant than the world of "sane" cultists.

So much for psychiatry and views of the Absurd World.

When a patient is very ill, and when he is violent, he must be treated. In cases where drugs are involved, treatment must be swift.

Adolescence is certainly a crisis period in any young life, but compound that phase of life with existence in a pressure-factory of a university and something can very definitely give. Owen's resistance to peer pressure gave out; he finally succumbed to group demands and began to smoke pot. The more tension (academic and social), the more pot. Until one night the pot that he regularly savored was spiked, unbeknownst to him, with PCP, commonly known as angel dust.

From pot to angel dust. The saga of a sophomore. And when that sophomore is a gifted young individual, it becomes all the more tragic. So, I read on. I must find out more about pot and PeaCe Pills.

Marijuana. So many beautiful things have been written about this little weed that it is now time to set the record straight. Marijuana (active hallucinogenic ingredient: tetrahydrocannabinol, or THC) is, according to recent writings by a number of eminent experts, "a very dangerous drug . . . far more hazardous than was originally suspected." These are the warning words of Professor George K. Russell, who goes on to tell us that THC is dangerous because the physical results to the human body from continued usage are cumulative.

Many people do not realize what a complex, yet delicate, organ the human brain actually is, nor do they understand the very careful balance of chemicals which must be continuously maintained in this three-pound organ in order for a person to function rationally.

Dr. Nathan Kline, the world-famous psychiatrist and drug pioneer (Thorazine), describes the functions and components of the brain in his book, *From Sad to Glad*. As he explains it, there are three substances involved in mental-emotional breakdowns: chemical compounds, salt compounds, and hormones.

The chemical compounds, called biogenic amines, are of the utmost concern to us here, for they regulate the nerve-call responses in the brain. There are three compounds involved, namely, norepinephrine, dopamine, and serotonin. Although there are a staggering 10 billion cells inside the brain, the amount of each of these chemicals is infinitesimal. Dopamine is the biogenic amine altered in drug-induced psychoses. The normal amount of this chemical in the brain is one-thirty thousandth of an ounce! Therefore, the ingestion of only a small quantity of a mind-altering drug, such as marijuana, can throw the minute dopamine level completely out of kilter, altering it and wreaking psychic havoc, or as Dr. Kline gently puts it, producing a "discord."

Professor Russell, familiar with brain chemistry, is deeply concerned. In his informative pamphlet, *Marijuana Today*, he cites both mental and physical health hazards which result from chronic usage of marijuana:

• Marijuana accumulates in the fatty tissues of the body, especially the brain and gonads (sex organs).

• When used, even in small doses, marijuana can result in severe "damage to the entire cellular process."

• Marijuana, after accumulating in the brain through heavy usage, causes cellular damage and can eventually lead to cerebral atrophy.

• Mental function diminishes, deteriorates, and "pathological forms of thinking resembling paranoia" can occur.

• Motivation is impaired and reduced, posing a serious threat to college students who are regular users.

Professor Russell cites many studies and experiments, some done in Canada, to which the reader may refer. Some skeptics may criticize that many of these studies have been done on monkeys. But monkeys are, after all, primates whose bodily functions closely parallel those in humans. The results obtained with marijuana are, therefore, as valid as those experiments which have shown cigarettes and saccharine to be carcinogens.

All the psychiatrists I have spoken to or whose books I have read come to the same conclusion: when used heavily over prolonged periods of time, marijuana becomes a hallucinogenic drug, causing behavior that can only be classified as psychotic. Mixed with angel dust, marijuana works that much faster to damage the delicate brain cells, causing the loss of sense of reality which is the precursor of psychosis.

Psychiatrists Kalansky and Moore state that the whole mental picture changes—reasoning ability is impaired, memory suffers, and the sense of time is distorted—this after prolonged use of pot. Plain pot.

The effect that marijuana has on any one person cannot be predicted, and the experts caution that a severe psychotic reaction can occur in an emotionally healthy person after only one dose. Combine pot with angel dust and you have a lethal concoction if ever there was one.

It is easy to see how a young person whose will power has been greatly diminished through heavy use of marijuana can drift into the use of angel dust. Psychic resistance is no longer there, so a stronger drug is substituted.

What about brain damage from continued use of pot? One expert, Dr. L.J. West, a psychiatrist from the University of Oklahoma Medical Center, speaks of the "biochemical scarring of the brain" from continued use of marijuana alone. These are strong words. Yet, we must listen.

Brain damage from prolonged use of pot may result because marijuana is fat soluble, in contrast to alcohol, which is water soluble. This means that alcohol is broken down into water and carbon dioxide through the body's metabolic process within several hours after intake. It is, for all intents and purposes, gone. Marijuana (THC), in contrast, accumulates in the fatty tissues of the central nervous system. Not only does the THC accumulate, but it lasts for long periods of time. Marijuana has a half-life of seven days, which means that one week after stopping its use, only half of the chemical is eliminated from the body. In short, the brain is bombed. Maybe permanently.

"Irreversible brain damage" has been described by Dr. N.A. Pace in *The Marijuana Health Hazard* as well as "brain atrophy (shrinkage)" after habitual use of the weed. Personality changes, the doctor states, can usually be noted in a user after only several months of steady use.

At this point, I cannot help thinking of the adults in my circle who brag about the "good" pot they smoke every night (as if there can ever be "good" pot). But I am older and, I hope, a little wiser than Owen. I can resist. Especially now, when I know the sobering facts.

Why then, I must wonder, are we so liberal minded about the use of marijuana in this country? And why do only positive reports get printed, while the appalling negative reports, especially those done in Canada, are suppressed or simply ignored by our newspaper and magazine editors? The reasons are many. And complex. Sociological, political, and economic.

We are a seemingly threatened people, living in a time of social unrest and upheaval. When the enormous defense budget is discussed, and an impressive array of formidable nuclear weapons is paraded before us, in all the media, it is a terrifying display. The Bomb is here to stay.

When cancer lurks in every breath of polluted air, in every processed food product, we become increasingly more disturbed, and seek means of relief.

Liquor is an outlet. Librium is an outlet. And marijuana is an outlet. All of these products provide instantaneous relief, short-lived though it might be. We now know that cigarettes kill. Yet more people than ever, younger and younger people, people who have had high school health courses, are inhaling deadly tobacco. For relief. For relaxation.

Another answer, or partial answer, to our national addiction to marijuana is provided for us in the International Drug Report. The explanation given here for suppressing negative facts about pot is a purely political one. "The potentially powerful eighteen-year-old vote has had its effect upon our legislators. And since drug abusers now come from all social strata, heavy penalties are no longer acceptable. No matter what, better education is a must." A must, the experts say. Let us hope that this education reaches the youngsters *before* they get up to the university level.

The true answer, my friends, is written in the economy. At the end of 1978, the three most important businesses in the United States of America, in order of importance, were Exxon, General Motors, and marijuana. And who supports this marijuana trafficking? Organized crime, of course. The profit? Billions of dollars. The loss? Brilliant minds in universities across the nation.

So, now we leave our political sea of pot and drift on to a more turbulent ocean. This time, man-made.

Insanity. It has been a frightening word all through the ages of mankind. It is a word that conjures up images, images of dementia, of possession, of devils and demons. And yet today we can manufacture it—with chemicals. Test-tube psychosis. Take the right combination of ingredients, mix and treat properly, and voila! Mania made to order.

This happened to Owen. Heavy pot smoking alone could have made him mentally ill. But there was something else. Something more potent. There was angel dust.

It looks like sugar—white, powdery, readily soluble in water. But you don't put it into your coffee, and you don't sprinkle it on your grapefruit. You smoke it, because it's faster—and, baby, you are in heaven. You're a heavenly angel. Or are you?

Phenyl-cyclohexyl-piperidine (PCP) was christened the PeaCe Pill by the love-hungry beatniks in the Haight-Ashbury district of San Francisco when they first discovered it.

The drug was developed originally as an anesthetic for humans in the 1950s under the brand name Sernyl by Parke, Davis & Company. After administering it to only a few patients (fortunately it was only a few), physicians noted adverse psychic side effects in their patients. As they came out of the anesthesia, the patients became increasingly agitated or delirious. In short, they did not behave normally. The anesthesiologists reported this, and the drug was taken off the human market; it was later remarketed, in liquid form, for veterinary use only, as an animal tranquilizer. New name: Sernylan. It is no longer being legally manufactured.

The "potential" of this drug did not pass unnoticed, however, and the beatniks of the fifties, ready for some new and glorious high, got the recipe and tried it out.

"It's the PeaCe Pill, man!" Yet, the PeaCe Pill was really not so peaceful after all. Strange things happened, like anxiety states that lasted too long, hallucinations that scared the living daylights out of one, and much unexpected fear and trembling. The beatniks collectively shuddered, and quickly dropped PCP.

What do we know now of the effects on the human body of PCP? Three successive stages have been noted by psychiatrists: Low dosage causes sedation, sleepiness, possible hallucinations. Moderate dosage causes severe hallucinations and psychosis. Heavy dosage causes—you guessed it!—convulsions, coma, and finally death from respiratory depression.

Let us dwell for a moment on the second stage effect. This is what has happened to Owen. Psychosis. Strikingly similar, especially to the untrained eye, to schizophrenia. Dr. Sidney Cohen of the Neuropsychiatric Institute describes it thusly: "Excited Catatonia—psychomotor agitation, incoherent profuse speech . . . unpredictable destructiveness . . . the internal mental events are so disturbing and without meaning that certain persons [like Owen] will respond running aimlessly [through the dorm halls] performing bizarre actions [with the fire extinguisher]."

In the medical publication *Clinical Toxicology* it has also been observed that the PCP psychosis resembles a combination of paranoid schizophrenia and catatonic excitement. Cases are noted here of young people running aimlessly and endlessly for many hours. In addition, when case histories were obtained, it was found that, in almost all cases, the users had had no history of psychological disorders.

The psychiatrists referred to above consider the early phase of PCP psychosis an emergency psychiatric situation. They describe the actual progress of the illness as three phases of equal length: 1) violent, agitated, psychotic behavior; 2) behavior more controlled, but restlessness is evident; and 3) personality reintegrates and thoughts become rational. It is interesting how psychiatrists are able to profile a specific drug-induced psychosis. And it is not a pretty picture.

Why, then, has angel dust made such a splashy comeback? We must conjecture that the public has not been presented with all the grisly facts, although angel dust is certainly now getting far more negative publicity than marijuana. At any rate, young people are probably quite ignorant of the medical data. They look, like the beatniks before them, for a fast and cheap "high" and, since PCP is relatively inexpensive and uncomplicated to produce, it is being manufactured in bathtubs all over this country.

Yes, it is back, often in poorly manufactured form. Angel dust, that white, innocent-looking substance, is clearly a misnomer. Devil dust it is, for sure.

My research is now complete. I do not have all the answers. I cannot see the difference between the Real World and the Absurd World. I do not know why people poison themselves with pot and PCP. But I have learned enough for my purposes.

I think of Owen. How he is now. And how he was then. I see the young men in his dorm urging him to try one reefer. He holds out. For months and months he resists. But the strong peer pressure is there. It is a fact of college life. Finally, he can take it no longer. He must join the others. I want to click off the camera of my mind, but I watch. In morbid fascination. Owen takes one puff, then another. He is urged to inhale. Reluctantly, he does. It is so easy to get hooked. Such a relaxing pastime. It now becomes a nightly habit. Owen smokes. And he writes poetry. He buys a pipe, to make it more effective. And then, late one night, he cannot sleep. He has just bought a new bag of marijuana. He opens it, fills his pipe, and sits down at his desk, puffing. He begins to shiver. Fear now grips him, but he writes. Poetry is the second best escape. The shivering continues, worsens. A friend calls for an ambulance. Owen is taken to the infirmary (it is several days before the onset of the actual psychosis). The bag of marijuana is now resting at the bottom of the wastebasket. It had been liberally laced with angel dust.

8

THE OPEN WARD

Up—up—away from the lower depths. At the twelfth floor of
the new building of the medical center, the elevator opens onto
a spacious reception room, walled in glass. There is a wide-
angle view of flat Long Island. On a clear day you can see the
Empire State Building, some twenty miles to the west. There
are spacious, well-lighted corridors, a large nurses' station where
the two wings, east and west, converge, glass-walled, impressive
and inaccessible. Nurses and records alike are hidden away from
view. A nurses' aide sits by the glass-enclosed counter. One must
talk through a small opening in the glass. It reminds me of a
bank. Remote. Cold.

Yet, Owen is on the mend, and we are all thinking positive.
He speaks, and his rich, well-modulated voice makes sense. He
acts, and his actions have purpose.

"Hi, Owen, how're you doing?"

"Hi. I'm fine."

I find him in the dayroom. It is a spacious room with several
picture windows. It is filled with tables and chairs, a phonograph,
records, and games. The patients eat here, and play cards or
other games. Off this room there is a carpeted television room.
And in the corridor off these rooms is a Ping-Pong table.

He is seated alone, looking through a magazine. His hands
shake as he turns the pages. I pretend not to notice.

"I'm so glad you're here now, Owen. It's so much nicer than Ward Ten, isn't it?"

"It certainly is." He smiles.

"May I see your room?"

"Sure."

We walk down the long corridor in the west wing. I observe that he is very stiff. His body still tilts forward, at about a twenty-degree angle. He cannot walk properly; he glides—and his entire body is shaking now. I remember the zombies. And I say nothing.

The room is at the end of the corridor. It is of moderate size. There are three beds, three night tables, a sink, a bathroom complete with shower, and best of all, a large picture window. The view of Long Island is impressive.

"I brought you some fresh clothes. I'll leave them by your bed."

Owen thanks me and proceeds to put the clothes in his night table. He can barely bend.

I notice that he is wearing the new slippers that I bought him. I am pleased. In Ward 10 he always seemed to be barefooted, and it had been so cold.

We spend the remainder of the afternoon in the dayroom. I chat, as lightly as possible, about the other children, their schools, their friends, and so on. Owen listens, politely.

Visiting hours are much more liberal on the twelfth floor. The entire setup here is psychologically beneficial to patient and visitors alike. Visiting hours are now twice a day. And the double doors leading from the main reception room are open. OPEN. At night, however, they are locked, and one must ring a bell for admission.

Some of the patients, I notice, are allowed to move about freely. They usually go down to the main-level coffee shop during the afternoon. Occasionally, I spot one, sitting alone, mumbling harmlessly.

There are, again, quite a few young patients here. One boy is in his early teens. Very few are middle-aged, which is surprising considering all the talk about "mid-life crisis" in our society. But there are about a dozen elderly, seemingly senile, patients in the ward who appear to be permanent residents. They are never visited, but sit, day after day, in wheelchairs in the main corridor, shouting repetitive phrases, all day long.

Owen is not quite up to socializing yet, although he is pleasant and lucid when Vincent and I visit.

On the second day in Ward O-P, his physical condition deteriorates further. He is so stiff now that he cannot turn over in bed. He is terribly uncomfortable. And yet, being Owen, he doesn't complain. Owen has now developed, it seems, acute parkinsonian-type symptoms.

I telephone Dr. Sand. Yes, he admits, the side effects from the Haldol are severe. They will gradually reduce the dosage and immediately administer counteractive medication: Cogentin (generic name, benztropine). Why, I wonder, have they waited so long?

On the next day, I notice a slight improvement in Owen's physical condition. But he is psychologically shaken. I think of a variation of an old expression: the drug cured the disease, but the patient died.

The nurse informs me, after I plead for information, that the Cogentin is administered by injection for the first few dosages. After that it is given in pill form.

I try to assist Owen as much as I can. It is especially difficult for him to minister to his own needs since he is shaking so much. Mealtime is a case in point. Each patient must get on line, pick up a food tray, and walk to a table. The theory, that each patient develop a sense of responsibility, is an excellent one. But if the patient is physically unable to manage, what then?

Today, I get on line with his tray. Owen is seated in the dayroom, waiting. An aide comes over to me.

"You can't do that!" she shouts.

"But my son is shaking. He can hardly walk!"

"He's supposed to do it himself," she admonishes me. Owen has gotten up and is coming over to the line. He has never liked stepping on anyone's toes. I give him the tray but keep one hand on it to steady it.

I speak to Dr. Sand every day on the telephone. I have not yet met him face to face.

"We are dropping the dosage of Haldol to twenty milligrams a day and then down to ten milligrams over the weekend. Along with the Cogentin, that should do the trick."

I mention my experience with the aide, the difficulty I have with the nurses.

"He is stiff," I tell him, "so stiff, in fact, that he cannot dress himself. The nurses seem unconcerned. All I see them do is put notes into the patients' records. Why can't they be of more assistance?"

"The staff is intolerant," the doctor informs me. Sadly, he seems to accept the fact.

"And what about his current mental illness?" I want to know.

"It was all drug-related," the doctor assures me. "All Owen will need is a low dosage of medication for the next few weeks."

I wonder, out loud, when he will be able to return home (where, I feel, he will be able to get better care). The doctor is noncommittal. "We'll see" is all he will say.

That evening, Owen makes a brave attempt to play a game of Ping-Pong with Fred, a young fellow patient. They are at it as Vince and I arrive for our visit.

"Hey, that's pretty good," I encourage.

Owen is so stiff he can hardly bend to retrieve the ball. I dash for it each time it hits the floor. After a few minutes he comes into the dayroom to sit with us.

"Well, that was a good volley you had going there," Vince says. He hands Owen the *Times* and *Newsday*.

"Yeah," Owen smiles. "I'm really out of practice."

"Well, you can practice a little each day," I say. I hand him a chocolate malted.

"How are you feeling now?" Vince asks. Casually.

"I'm feeling all right. I guess."

"You're doing just fine," I encourage. "I spoke to Dr. Sand and he says you're coming along just fine."

"Yeah." He drinks the malted.

The nurse enters with a Monopoly game. "Anyone for Monopoly?" she asks. Several young people go over to her table.

"Do you want to play?" Vince asks.

"No. I'll just look at the papers," Owen replies. He leafs aimlessly through them. For his father's benefit.

"Look, Owen," I tell him, "tomorrow is Saturday and I have to work. Dad will be here in the afternoon and I'll come in the evening. Okay?"

"Okay."

We spend a few more pleasant moments with our son and then the announcement is made that visiting hours are over. I kiss him good-night and wave from the doorway of the day-room.

Vincent and I have to wait for an orderly to come and unlock the double doors. I say nothing until we get to the elevator bank.

"I'm concerned about the stiffness and the shaking."

"Look," Vince replies, "I'll be here with him tomorrow afternoon. I'll keep a close eye on him and help him as much as possible."

I shake my head in disbelief.

"What's the matter?" he asks. "Didn't the doctor tell you that he's getting better?"

"Yes."

"Isn't he acting and talking normally now?"

"Yes, but what good is it if he looks like a zombie?"

"Stop it, Ursula. We have to have confidence in the doctors."

"Do we?"

Now Vincent shakes his head and walks rapidly ahead of me across the lobby of the hospital.

That night I cannot sleep.

9

STEPPING BACKWARD

On Saturday morning I leave for work early. It is a crisp, sunny November day. And as I drive along, I find myself in a surprisingly optimistic mood. My fears of the previous evening have fled, displaced by the sun. There is, I am convinced, a psychology of Time: daylight = brightness and happiness; nighttime = darkness and despair. Why are so many people, droves of people, today settling in the sun belt? Because the northern winter days are short and depressing, the biting cold irritating. The sun is not only physically beneficial, it is emotionally beneficial, as well. The gray, overcast skies of New York are hardly cheering. But today, today is different. There is a bright blue Floridian sky—and things are looking up.

But it's not only the sunshine that cheers me on. It's the beautiful place I work in with beautiful people in a suburban town that, too, can only be described as beautiful. My job, with an elegant home furnishing chain, is cushiony. I am happy here.

This position is just right for me, for the moment. The manager of the showroom is kind and understanding; my co-workers are fine, sympathetic people. Everyone knows that my son is ill and in the hospital. But I do not discuss the nature of his illness. I cannot discuss it. The stigma is there. Mental illness, no matter what its origin, is a darkness, a horror, not to be mentioned.

And drugs? One cannot comfortably speak of their use—and especially not of their abuse.

So I choose not to discuss the nature of my son's long illness. And the beautiful people say not a word.

Today I have informed the children that I will not be home for dinner, but will go straight to the hospital from work. Vincent will be coming home at that time, and will have dinner with them.

During my daily phone conversations with Dr. Sand I have taken notes on the progress of Owen's illness. At night I transfer these notes to my diary. But today is Saturday and Dr. Sand always has weekends and holidays off. A substitute (resident) physician will be taking his place. No matter. Owen is on the mend. I dismiss these thoughts and totally absorb myself in my work.

At two o'clock there is a telephone call for me from the hospital. It is Vincent.

"We've had a little accident here."

"What do you mean?" I grip the edge of my desk.

"I left Owen alone for a few minutes—I wanted to get him a milk shake in the coffee shop—and when I came back he had fallen on his head."

"How bad is it?"

"I don't know."

"I don't understand how this could happen in a hospital in the middle of the day."

"He was trying to get dressed by himself. He's still too stiff to move, and he got dizzy, lost his balance, and fell. I found him lying in a pool of blood."

"Oh, God!"

"It wasn't from his head. The fall caused a nosebleed. But they have to find out if he injured his skull. They've just wheeled him downstairs to x-ray."

"I simply can't believe this!"

"I just wanted you to know what happened before you come later—"

"I'm not coming later I'm coming now!"

I dash out, telling my manager that an emergency has just occurred and I must get over to the hospital.

Vincent greets me in the twelfth-floor reception room.

"He's resting now. He's been badly shaken and they've got him in a private room right behind the nurses' station, so they can check on him."

"That's good."

"He's not supposed to move out of bed."

"Look, Vince, you go and stay with him. I want to speak to the charge nurse."

We part and I go over to the nurses' station and ask for the head nurse. She comes out, reluctantly.

"He'll have to stay perfectly still for twenty-four hours now. And we're putting him on a liquid diet," she informs me.

"I can see why," I tell her, no longer masking my annoyance. "He shakes so much he can't lift a tray."

"We'll help him with his meals today," she says.

"Why wasn't he helped before, when he tried to get dressed?"

"We didn't know he needed help," she replies lamely.

"And what about the X rays?"

"We won't have the results until tonight."

"I see. And what about his medication?"

"I'm really not supposed to discuss that."

"What doctor is treating him now?"

The resident on duty. Dr. Movar."

"Where is he? Can I speak to him now?"

"It's a she. I'll have to call downstairs and see if she'll come up to talk to you."

"Please!" I implore.

A few minutes later, a young Indian woman approaches me.

"I'm Dr. Movar. I understand you want to speak with me about your son."

"Yes, doctor. I'm concerned about my son's fall. I know the Haldol has caused these terrible side effects—and yet, it helped him get well, mentally. Is he still getting the Cogentin?"

"Yes. We've just given him another injection. He had been on the pill form; the injection will act much faster."

"Doctor, I don't want him to have a relapse. Please, please keep him on the Haldol and the Cogentin."

"I'm on duty here today. I will make the decision."

"Is there any way I can reach Dr. Sand? I'd really like to discuss this with him."

"There's no way to reach him. Anyway, I am on duty here, and I will determine the medication."

"Please, doctor, please keep him on the Haldol until Dr. Sand can see him on Monday."

"Mrs. Etons, I am the resident and I will decide what is best for the patient."

It is no use. I am getting nowhere. Uneasily, I turn away from her and head for Owen's new room.

Vince is standing, protectively, in the doorway.

"Shush," he whispers, index finger pressed to his lips. "He's resting quietly now."

"Is he asleep?"

"I don't think so. But his eyes are closed."

I move close to the bed. The side rails are up. It appears to me that this hospital takes care of problems after the fact.

"Hi, Owen," I kiss his forehead lightly.

He opens his eyes. He is very pale and listless.

"Hi." There is no smile today.

"I'm sorry you got hurt," I tell him. "But you'll be all right now. I just spoke to the doctor."

He says nothing. His eyes stare blankly at the ceiling.

"This new room is very nice," I continue. It is small, but there is a large window and a private bath.

I sit down by his bed. His hands are shaking. I put my hand over them.

"I'm very nervous," he tells me.

"No, you're not nervous at all. It is the medication that is making you shake like this. That's what made you dizzy in the first place. But you're getting something now that will make these side effects go away."

He says nothing.

We sit in silence as the short November day darkens and withers away, taking with it the promise of the morning.

A nurse breezes in at 5 P.M. "It's dinnertime," she announces, cheerily. She sets the tray down on a tall table on wheels and brings it over to the bed. "We'll crank up your bed now so that you can eat," she tells Owen.

I watch as she feeds him some soup. There is also juice and Jell-O on the tray, as well as a can of ginger ale.

"I'm not really very hungry," Owen tells her.

"Well," she says, sticking a straw into his ginger ale, "I'll just leave these things here then. You can have them later." She sets the food down on the night table and whisks herself out with the tray.

It is dark now.

"I'm very tired," Owen says.

"Why, of course," I tell him. "You've had a fall and now you have to get some rest. But just think, by tomorrow at this time you'll be walking again."

"Yeah. I'll be walking again." He is unconvinced.

"Listen, Dad and I will be leaving soon. We want you to get a good night's sleep. But tomorrow I will be here all day, and Marc and Marsha will be here, too. They're on Long Island for the weekend."

"That's nice," he says, without enthusiasm.

I kiss him good-night, and Vince and I head for the nurses' station.

"We'd like to get the results of the X rays taken of my son," he tells the nurse on duty.

"You'll have to go down to Psych E-R," she informs us.

Vince and I head for the lower depths, as I now think of it. Once let in, we are told that we must wait. The results have not yet come in. It is nearly seven o'clock.

We sit on one of the wooden benches in the corridor. As we are waiting, there is a loud knock on the double doors and the nurse on duty admits two policemen who are "escorting" a young, unkempt man. He has to be forced to sit on one of the chairs. The officers fill out some forms, speak to the nurse on duty, and leave.

I take a hard look at this new, involuntary patient and wonder what has triggered his episode. He is oblivious to all but his most inner urgings. And they are violent urgings, for he is now standing and screaming, face mottled, at the top of his lungs, "Get me out of here!" He curses intermittently. His vocabulary of four-letter words is impressive.

"Sit down, Randolph," the nurse admonishes. "Sit down now and be good."

"I ain't sittin' down, you lousy cunt!" he protests. "I ain't stayin' in this looney bin! I want out!"

"Quiet, Randolph," the nurse insists. "If you don't sit down and be quiet, I'm going to have to give you a shot."

"A shot!" He comes to the side of the nurses' counter. "Okay, you can give me a shot." He lowers his trousers and bends over, invitingly. The nurse smiles, shakes her head, and goes over and helps him up with his pants. I look away.

Several more minutes elapse and then the psychiatrist on duty comes out of the office and sits at the nurses' counter. I suspect he has been alerted to Randolph's antics.

I recognize this middle-aged doctor. I have often seen him on the twelfth floor and I have been favorably impressed with him. He has always seemed so pleasant to the patients. I got up and go over to speak to him.

"Doctor, we are waiting here for X ray results. My son had a fall this morning." I proceed to give him the details. As I am standing opposite him, the distraught Randolph jumps up, runs over to the counter next to me, and begins pounding on it and shouting.

"I want to get outa here!"

Vincent pulls me away.

The nurse comes hurriedly out of her station. Randolph is now stalking back and forth wildly, cursing loudly as he goes. A male orderly is sent for. As soon as he arrives, they both try, unsuccessfully, to subdue Randolph.

In the meantime, the psychiatrist (who has never lost *his* composure) receives a phone call from the X ray department. He calls us both over to the counter.

"Well, I have very good news for you. The X rays are negative."

"Thank you," I say, very softly. I can hardly speak. Vince leans over the counter to shake the psychiatrist's hand.

The nurse on duty says she will unlock the door for us. She leaves Randolph with the orderly, who is still trying to get him in the examining room for his shot. As the door is opened for us, Randolph suddenly bolts out the door and down the corridor to the nearest outside exit. The nurse runs to the outer door, but Randolph has disappeared into the night.

10

NURSING

On Sunday, I become Owen's private nurse. I work a full nine-hour shift. Motivation: love. Remuneration: rapid improvement of patient, both physically and mentally.

I sneak into the hospital early. It is 11 A.M. and although visiting hours do not officially begin until one o'clock, the double doors to Ward O-P are wide open. No one attempts to stop me as I walk through, assuredly, to Owen's private room.

He is lying in bed. Very still. As I go over to him, he smiles. I am, at once, encouraged.

"Well," I say, "you look much better today."

"I feel a little better."

"Let me crank up the bed so that you can see the view."

"Not too much," he warns.

I place my hands on his shoulders. He is still shaking slightly. I begin to massage his shoulders and arms.

"That feels pretty good," he tells me.

"And it's good for you, too. It gets the blood circulating."

For the remainder of the morning, I massage his shoulders, arms, and hands.

The nurse brings in his liquid lunch. Although it is only noon, she does not comment on my early presence in the room.

"I'll help him with his lunch," I offer. She is only too happy to accommodate me. I crank up the head of the bed to a ninety-degree angle and place the tray in front of my patient. He is not too enthused with the prospect of another liquid meal, but I lend some encouragement.

"C'mon, have some soup. It will give you strength." It isn't even chicken soup, I note, but I assist him with it, anyway. He is able to hold his juice glass, although his hand still shakes somewhat. The Jell-O he tackles alone.

"Look," I tell him, "I've brought my own sandwich. This way I don't have to go down to the coffee shop. I'd much prefer staying with you." He offers me some ginger ale, which I accept.

"When is Dad coming?" he asks, pushing the tray away.

"He'll be here in a little while with Suzy. Tim is too young. They won't let him in."

"Too bad. I'd like to see him."

"I know. But the good news is that Marc and Marsha will be here today. They're going back to school tomorrow."

"That's nice." He is lost in thought for a minute. "Did they get all of my things up at college?" It is the first time he has mentioned college.

"Yes, they brought everything home. It's all in your room."

"What about my guitar?"

"Oh, yes. Of course they brought that."

"I'd really like my guitar. Do you think you could bring it here?"

"Well, I'll have to find out."

"I'd rather go home and practice. When do you suppose I'll be able to leave here?"

"I don't know. But I will speak to Dr. Sand tomorrow. You'll be seeing him, too. You could ask him yourself." I am pleased that he wants to go home. It is a good sign.

"Yeah. I'd really like to leave."

"I'm sure it won't be much longer. You're so much better now. I've seen a tremendous improvement in just the last couple of hours."

"I hope so." He closes his eyes.

"Would you like to take a little nap now? The medicine may be making you sleepy. Did you get any this morning?"

"I got one shot—I don't know what else."

"That's good. It will help you. Look, let me lower your bed and you take a little rest." I crank down the head of the bed.

Owen appears to be sleeping. I slip off my shoes and walk over to the window. I lean against the cold glass, peering down the twelve stories to the suburban streets below. Straight lines intersecting at right angles, rows of tiny boxes, several million people spread out on an island 150 miles long. The window faces south, and in the far distance, I think I can make out the obelisk at Ocean Beach, on the Atlantic Ocean. Yes, Long Island looks impressive from this vantage point. Tiny toy towns, tiny motorcars moving mechanically, tiny boxes housing invisible doll-sized people, all going through the motions of living.

I look up now. Away from my toy topography. The sky is somewhat overcast. A typical New York sky. More white than blue, almost always hazy. Polluted. I long for Florida. "The sunniest state east of the Mississippi" the *Encyclopaedia Britannica* has said. "The Sunshine State" proudly emblazoned on every license plate. Well named. Round golden sun, set like a giant canary diamond in a jewel-blue sky . . . towering royal palms . . . white foaming ocean pounding the sand at Palm Beach. I wonder now if Dr. Sand would let me take Owen to Florida this winter. I still have the house. It is furnished and empty. Waiting. It would be so beneficial. It would hasten the healing. For both of us. . . .

Turning away from the window, I sit down on the vinyl armchair in the corner of the room. And I contemplate this place. It has now become nearly as dismal as Psych E-R. My mind returns to the previous evening. I am grateful for one thing. Randolph is now here, in Ward O-P, not out on the loose. I spotted him as I passed the nurses' station. Two nurses were discussing sending him down to Ward 10. Poor Randolph, I expect his cursing is quite disconcerting to them.

Owen stirs awake as Vincent arrives with Suzy. It is now two o'clock. Suzy is delighted to see her brother again. She kisses him and he perks up immediately.

Marc and Marsha enter the room. "We met in the parking lot," Vince explains.

It is the first time that Marc has seen his brother since he brought him home from the university. I am somewhat dismayed by the fact that he has to see him, immobilized, after his setback. But at least he is rational, not delusional.

Marc walks over to the bed. "How're you doing?"

"Okay, now. Thanks."

Marsha plants a kiss on his cheek. "You look fine."

"Yeah. Thanks. But I'm still a little nervous." He hides his shaking hands under the covers.

"He's not nervous at all," I assure them. "It's just the medication. He's had a bad reaction."

"Hey," Owen says, trying to change the subject, "I hear that you brought back my guitar."

"Sure did. When are you going to play again?" Marc asks.

"Gee, I don't know. Probably when I get home."

"That'll be great."

"Yeah. I should be going home soon. I'm going to speak to the doctor tomorrow."

"Don't rush things," Marsha cautions. She cannot easily forget her mad ride in President Carter's motorcade.

"No. I'm not rushing things," Owen states. "I'm much better now." He tries to sit up, straining himself.

"Here, let me crank up your bed," Suzy says, putting him into a more comfortable position.

Vince walks over to the bed. "I brought you the Sunday *Times*. It's all there, except the business section." He places the bulky paper on the tray at the foot of his bed.

Owen makes no move. "I don't know if I'll be able to read it just yet."

Vincent doesn't want to recognize the fact that Owen's powers of concentration have been temporarily impaired.

"Don't worry," Vince says, "I'll just leave it here, and when you feel like reading, you'll read it."

The afternoon is spent in pleasant conversation, each person picking a topic of special interest. College (Marc), football (Vince), cheerleading (Suzy). Safe, innocuous subjects.

I have grown happy here, in this little private room, behind the nurses' station, far away from the bustle of the day-room and the TV room. It is remote enough so that we can talk without interruption. There are no other patients to distract us and the staff leaves us alone.

It is nearly dusk now, and Marc and Marsha get up to leave.

"Well, kiddo," Marc tells his brother, "next time I'm home, I expect to find you plucking away at them there guitar strings."

"Righto." They shake hands.

"Have a good, safe trip back," I say, kissing them both good-bye. Vince and Suzy leave with them.

"Well," I turn to Owen who is sitting up in bed. "I think you might try to walk a little now."

"Good idea," he agrees.

He gets slowly out of bed and I notice that he is standing straighter. The shaking has almost completely disappeared. He walks over to the window and looks out at the darkening sky.

"It's a nice view," he comments. "I think I can see the Ocean Beach obelisk from here."

I go over and put my arm around his shoulder. "Yes, Owen, I'm glad you noticed that."

"Do you suppose I could get out of this room for a while? I feel cooped up in here."

"Sure. Let's go out in the corridor and get some exercise."

I help him on with his bathrobe, he is still slightly stiff, and we go out into the corridor behind the nurses' station.

As we are walking, one of the nurses spots us.

"Hey!" she calls out. "What are you doing out of bed? No one told you to get up yet. Now," she says, directly to Owen, "you'll have to go back to your regular room."

She is punishing us, but I don't say anything. I liked the little private room. It enabled me to be with Owen for the entire day. But I dare not say anything. For Owen's sake.

The nurse sends an orderly into the room to move the bed back to the other, semi-private, room.

It is now suppertime. We both enter the dayroom where all the patients have assembled. Food is brought, on a multitiered wagon, into the corridor. Owen gets up, goes over to get his tray, and brings it back to the table. He is able to eat a regular meal without assistance.

"You're doing just fine, now," I tell him. "I see a tremendous improvement." He smiles as he finishes his ice cream.

"That was a pretty good dinner." He gets up, slowly, and takes his tray out to the corridor, stopping to say hello to other patients on the way. He is walking erect.

After dinner, Owen decides to watch the news. He is a student of history and world news has always been important to him. We go into the television room together. It is quite dark in this room; the only light emanates from the television set itself. There is blue carpeting on the floor, evidently to cushion the noise, and a row of blue contemporary armchairs line the wall opposite the large TV set, high up on the wall. Owen sits down on the chair next to mine. The news tonight is rather boring. Within five minutes he is up again. I wonder if it is the news or his own inner restlessness.

"Please," I urge, "sit down for a while."

"Okay," he agrees. But it is no use. Within a very few minutes he is up and walking about. I follow him out into the corridor. We stroll up and down the east wing, then the west wing, stopping occasionally to greet another patient. They all seem fond of Owen.

I follow him into the main corridor. There is no question now. Owen has become increasingly restless. Is it the illness or the medication that is causing this hyperactivity? I wonder.

Several minutes later, I am seated on a metal folding chair, in the main corridor of Ward O-P, witnessing a Ping-Pong game. Owen has gotten Lydia, one of the other young patients, to play a game with him. He is definitely improved, physically. I can see it in his serves. His strength is coming back; Lydia has trouble returning the serves. She is a cheerful, pleasant young woman. I wonder what has brought her here.

After the game, Owen and I again attempt to watch some television. Tom, one of the other young patients, offers Owen a cigarette. To my surprise, he accepts. I find a book of matches and light their cigarettes. But the tobacco does not relax him. Within five minutes he is up and about again.

We continue our stroll. Owen turns to me. "You know," he says, "I wasn't always very nice up at school."

"That isn't true," I reply. "You've always been a nice person."

But that isn't what he is talking about. He is obviously alluding to drugs. I say no more on the subject. What is there to say now?

It is eight o'clock and visiting hours are ending. Owen appears to be very tired. I walk him to his room.

Owen's bed is against the wall nearest the corridor. "Please get a good night's sleep," I say, as I prepare to tuck him in for the night. "Here," I caution, "move in a little closer to the wall [the fall of the previous day haunts me] you're on the edge."

"I *am* on the edge," Owen informs me. "I'm on the edge of health."

11

ON THE EDGE OF HEALTH

"He's been taken off medication," Dr. Sand says.

"What do you mean? The Haldol?"

"Yes."

"When?"

"On Saturday. After his fall. The resident thought it best."

"But I spoke to her," I remonstrate. "I specifically asked her not to. I told her to speak to you—"

"Well, she was in charge for the weekend and she thought, considering his side effects and the resulting fall, that it was the best thing to do."

"Doctor, he might just very well have a relapse without any medication."

"We're watching him very closely."

"That isn't good enough. I tell you he is restless—"

"Mrs. Etons, let's see what happens."

I cannot accept this attitude. But what good does this after-the-fact protesting do? None, obviously.

"He wants to go home," I say. Now I definitely want him at home.

"Yes, I know. He told me this morning."

"When do you think he can be discharged?"

"Oh, this week. Definitely. He'll be able to leave before the week is out. Probably on Thursday. I'll meet with you just before that. On Wednesday."

I am anxious to meet with Dr. Sand. To see that soothing voice, face to face.

Yet, after our phone conversation, I am uneasy. Owen is still restless. He cannot sit for even five minutes. The major tranquilizer had not only brought back his rationality, it had quieted him. And if they had given him the Cogentin from the very beginning, there wouldn't have been these horrendous side effects. If . . .

It is no use thinking about it. I must have confidence in the hospital. In the doctor.

I tell Owen the good news.

"You may be going home this week."

"Great! What day?"

"Well, possibly Thursday. But don't count on it. The doctor will make the final decision."

"I'll call Dad later and tell him."

"That will be nice."

We are sitting at a small table in the dayroom. Owen looks much better. The color has returned to his cheeks. The shaking has subsided. He appears to be pleasant, communicative. However, some of his thoughts disturb me. He is looking through last night's newspaper.

"There's going to be another war," he informs me. "There's going to be World War Three, no question about it."

"What makes you say that?"

"It's that hotbed in the Middle East. It's bound to start there."

"Oh, there's always been fighting in the Middle East. For centuries. You know that. You're a student of history."

"Yes. True. But now it's different. Now the Russians have the Bomb. And they're bound to start World War Three."

"I'm sure your fears are unfounded," I say.

His look is intense. "We have to watch out for the Russians," he warns.

Tom, another young patient, comes over to our table.

"Hey, man, you got a cigarette?"

"No," Owen replies, "but I'd sure like a cigar." He laughs. Tom returns a few minutes later and hands Owen a cigarette. "Got a match?" Tom asks me.

"Sure, sure." I start taking all of the miscellaneous goodies out of my large handbag. And there, under all of my nonessential things, is an untouched book of matches, a souvenir from a recent restaurant dinner. I light their cigarettes and stuff the matches back in my handbag.

"Listen, Mom," Owen states, "I'd really like some little cigars. Can you bring me a couple of packs?"

"Cigars?" I am appalled, but I force a smile. "Yes, what kind would you like?"

"Oh, Tiparillos will be fine."

I take notes.

"Yeah, but you can't get them at the coffee shop downstairs," Tom adds. "They don't sell tobacco in the hospital."

"Really?" I ask, facetiously. "I wonder why."

"There's a little tobacco shop right across the street," Tom continues. "You can see it if you look out that window there." He points and I get up and look down, across the wide main road that fronts the hospital. Sure enough, there is a little tobacco shop with a disproportionately large sign, evidently so that all in the hospital can see it.

"When I come back tonight I will bring you some little cigars. You know, of course, that I can't leave you any matches."

"The nurse has the matches," Tom states.

Owen gets up. He is still restless, although he appears to be able to sit for longer periods of time.

That evening I return, with Tiparillos. Owen is pleased. He is now a full-fledged smoker of cigars. I ply him now, and each day that follows, with mini-cigars. Tiparillos, Cigarillos, Muriel Air Tips. I feel like an accomplice as I light them for him.

"They relax me," he says.

God only knows, I want him to be relaxed.

We are in the dayroom and as we sit and chat, the nurse enters. She holds up a game and announces, "Pokeno!" (It resembles Bingo.) "Okay," she proclaims, "the winner receives a pack of cigarettes." She holds up a pack of Salem.

Owen joins the group and they begin the game. The nurse calls out a number, and each player with that particular number puts a disk on his large card. Owen gets a straight diagonal. He is declared the winner. The nurse ceremoniously hands him the cigarettes. He stashes the pack away in his shirt pocket. They will be traded, later that evening, for a pack of cigars.

Late that night, I speak to Vincent. "Owen was much better today."

"You don't have to tell me," he says. "He called me at my office."

"That's a good sign of improvement. What did he say?"

"That he's coming home this week."

"Yes, the doctor says he's doing very well. But—I'm a little worried. They took him off the Haldol on Saturday."

"Look, Ursula, we've got him in a big medical center. They must know what they're doing."

"*Big* doesn't always mean *best*. I'm not so sure they know what they're doing. He's still acting strangely . . ."

"What are you talking about?"

"First of all, he's still a bit jumpy, he's smoking these terrible little cigars—but then—then there are the Russians."

"The Russians?" Vince shakes his head.

"Yes. He's terribly worried about them."

"What's wrong with that?" he quips. "So's the president."

"Vince, please don't jest. I tell you there's still something wrong."

Vince smiles and goes into the bedroom. I am left, sitting alone, with my thoughts.

"I'm in physical therapy," Owen informs me the next day. He is dressed in street clothes, a pleasant change from the usual pajamas and robe.

"That's excellent," I reply. "What do you do?"

"I don't know, exactly. I won't start till later today. I think we make things. I saw some guys working with copper."

"That's terrific. Will you make something for me?"

"I'll try. If my hand doesn't shake."

"Why," I take his hand in mine, "you're not shaking at all, anymore. Of course you'll be able to make something. You know, you've always been artistic. It will be fun to be creative again."

"Yeah. I guess I'll try."

We spend the lunch hour together. After the meal I hand him two packs of cigars.

"Here, I got you some Tiparillos."

"Thanks." He takes one out and puts it in his mouth.

"Let me light it for you."

He puffs away, happily. I watch, but it is difficult for me. Blond, boyish Owen, puffing away like some old man. Incredible. Does the tobacco really fill a need? As I think about this, I see Harry, one of the elderly patients, approach. The cigar smoke has attracted his attention. And he is barking. Not a very good sign. It seems that Harry barks every time he wants a cigarette—and, for some reason, he is forbidden to have them.

"Arf-arf!" He puts his hand out to Owen.

"Hi, Harry. I don't have any cigarettes today. Just cigars. Besides, you're not supposed to smoke, anyway."

"Arf-arf!" Harry replies.

Owen stands firm as an orderly comes over and leads Harry, barking louder than ever, away.

When I return to work, I telephone the hospital, only to be in for a disappointment. Dr. Sand is not in today. It is Election Day and he has every holiday off. It is a very good union, I muse.

That evening, I return to the hospital. I find Owen in the TV room.

"It's good to find you watching some TV," I say.

"I'm watching quite a bit now," he states. "Do you know that last night I stayed up until midnight and watched the football game?"

"Really? And the nurses let you stay up that late?"

"Yeah. There were just a handful of us and we were quiet."

"That's good, Owen. That's very good."

Perhaps my fears concerning his restlessness have been unjustified. This news brightens me up considerably.

"Who wants to play horseshoes?" The nurse sticks her head into the TV room.

"I'll play." Owen gets up.

The nurse has set up the pins at one end of the long main corridor. Owen is joined by two other young male patients. They play quietly for a few minutes. It is hardly a challenging game, hitting these light plastic pins. Owen quits and we go into the dayroom together.

Lydia comes over to him.

"Hey, Owen, you look great today. You know that?"

"Thanks."

"Listen, we're playing Monopoly now and we need a fourth. How about it?"

"Okay." He excuses himself and joins the other young people for the Monopoly game.

As I sit nearby, watching these young people play, as I see how absorbed Owen has become in this classic game, I chide myself for the fears that I felt on the previous evening. He's better now. No question about it.

The nurse comes back in and announces that visiting hours are over. It is 8 P.M. I say good-night to Owen and the others and walk down the long corridor toward the elevators. Mrs. Harris, one of the older patients, stops me before the doors are unlocked. "He's doing much better," she tells me.

Yes, I'm glad the patients notice the improvement. They seem to be more sensitive to the nuances involved in mental illness than the nurses. Nevertheless, tomorrow is Wednesday. And tomorrow I am determined to meet with Dr. Sand. Face to face.

He is young. Very young—maybe thirty. Tall and lanky, with soft brown hair, sympathetic eyes, horn-rimmed glasses. He looks very professional in his white coat.

"Sit down here, Mrs. Etons," he directs me.

We are in one of the empty private rooms on O-P. We each sit down on the single bed in the room. Face to face.

"Well, I'm happy to tell you that Owen is fine, now. In fact, he is ready to go home. Tomorrow."

"And I am very happy to hear that," I reply. "My only concern, of course, is medication. I still feel that he would be much safer with it."

"Mrs. Etons, there is no need to give him any medication at all right now. We will assign him to a psychiatrist in the clinic. He can be seen there once a week, and if there is any indication for medication, it will be given to him."

"I don't know—"

"Believe me, Mrs. Etons, this will be the best path to follow. You must remember that this has been drug-induced, this illness. The drugs are now out of his system and he has had strong medication to counteract the deleterious effect that they have had on his brain."

"I wish you could tell me more—you know, how it all happened—"

"It was, as I may have indicated to you in our earlier conversations, the result of very strong peer pressure up at the university. Peer pressure can be a very devastating force."

"Yes. I've learned that."

"Living at home will be the best thing for him."

"Has he spoken to you about college—and the future?"

"Yes. And I very strongly suggested that he transfer to one of the fine universities here on Long Island."

"I'm very glad that you did. That's exactly what my husband and I want him to do."

He takes my hand in his. "Don't worry so much. Things will be all right now."

"Yes, doctor. I hope you're right."

I leave the interview with a strange, gnawing feeling in my stomach. And yet, Dr. Sand had been so firm, so assured . . . why am I so apprehensive? . . . I shrug off these negative thoughts and head for home.

———

That evening, Vince and I tell Owen the good news.

"You'll be coming home tomorrow." Vince beams as he hands him the day's newspapers.

"Can't wait," he says, puffing on a fresh cigar. He turns, intently, through the pages of the *Times*, stopping briefly to read a news article. "It's going to start. No question about it."

"What's going to start?" Vince asks.

"World War Three. The Russians are ready."

On the way home from the hospital I bring up the question of custodial care. "You know, I can take a long four-day weekend, but what am I going to do on Monday?"

"You mean with Owen?"

"Yes. You know he can't be alone. Not now."

"We'll have to get someone to stay with him."

"Yes, but who?"

"I don't know. Let me think."

I am deeply concerned. Not with the fact that Owen will return to drugs. That, I am convinced, is a thing of the past. My concern is more terrifying than that. I fear for a relapse. I dare not tell Vincent.

"How about Harriet Marshall?" he asks. "She's home all the time now. Maybe she can help us out, just in the interim."

"Yes. That's a good idea. I'll give her a call in the morning."

Harriet Marshall is the wife of a client of my husband's. She lives in the next town. I have not actually met her, but have spoken to her several times on the phone and we have had some pleasant conversations. She is a housewife, the mother of two teenage sons. And she has time and is willing to help. That is most important. She has agreed to come and stay with Owen on Monday and for as long as I need her. I have promised to try to find someone else.

Things are definitely looking up now. After seventeen days in the hospital, Owen is coming home.

12

HOME, BUT NOT FREE

Owen is waiting in the main lobby of the hospital as I enter. It is a pleasant surprise to see him there. Before we leave, I decide to speak once more with Dr. Sand. We go up to Neurology.

"I'm really concerned about Owen," I tell him privately. "I'd like to have some medication for him before I leave."

"I'd rather not give you anything at this time. Let's just wait and see how he does. I've made an appointment for him in the outpatient clinic for next Tuesday. He'll be seeing Dr. Bussoni."

"A psychiatrist?"

"Yes."

"Male or female?"

"Female. Does it matter?"

"No, I was just curious. Now, I assume that she will be able to give him a prescription, if necessary."

"Of course. But let's think positive. Let's hope for the best."

Owen is unhappy waiting. He wants to get out of the hospital as quickly as possible. Who can blame him?

As we leave the hospital grounds, I want to celebrate. To rejoice. The crisp fall air cheers me on. There is a park nearby. I stop the car near a long row of flower beds. The variety of colors is dazzling.

"I must pick some flowers," I tell Owen. "They're so bright and beautiful."

We get out of the car and I rush to the marigolds. Gleefully, I flit from flower bed to flower bed, like a busy bumblebee, plucking the fat marigolds, zinnias, petunias, and shasta daisies.

Owen watches. In silence.

I offer him the fresh, colorful bouquet. "Shall I get some more?"

"I want to go home."

Of course. He has been confined for seventeen days and now he wants to go home.

"I'm sorry, Owen. I thought you would like to spend a little time in the park. The air is so clean—and the trees and flowers look so lovely in the fall. Come on, let's go home."

We get into the car. Owen's face has grown serious. And he is restless. I am concerned. Is the angel dust still lurking there? In the deep crevices of his brain? Think positive, I tell myself. Owen is here. And now, we are going home together. I lay the bright bouquet on the front seat between us and start the engine.

Owen's mood seems to change for the better as soon as we arrive home. He spends time in his room, listening to music, resting, occasionally glancing at a magazine. It is difficult for him to read for any protracted length of time.

Suzy and Tim are delighted to have their brother home. Surprisingly, they had not spoken much of him while he was in the hospital. I attribute this to the trauma both suffered when they experienced his condition during that strange night and day preceding his hospital admission. It was such a shock for them, so incomprehensible, that the event was immediately repressed. "I'm making you a treat for dinner tonight," Suzy declares. "Moo goo gai pan." She is the cook in the family.

This evening is a happy occasion for us. We are all together again. It is quiet and peaceful. And, for the first time in eighteen days, I am able to sleep the whole night through.

Friday is another pleasant day. I supply Owen with records, books, magazines, and, of course, there is the television. I try my best to keep him occupied.

Yet he is somewhat restless. This must be, I rationalize, a rather dull life in comparison with the one he led at the university. College life is highly structured. There is the daily routine: classes, lectures, interesting special events. But here at home there is nothing specific for him to do but get well.

In the evening, Vince takes Owen and Tim to the movies. When they get home, Owen appears to be tired. But he is in good spirits.

The weekend goes smoothly. I am able to work a full day on Saturday, since Vincent is home with the children. And Sunday is a fine, happy family day for us. When I contrast this day with the previous Sunday, with Owen lying so sick in bed, I am extremely grateful to have him home. We have all slept late, and spend a lazy day with the Sunday *Times* and television.

On Monday, Harriet arrives to stay with Owen. She is a warm, pleasant woman, and it is good to have her here to keep an eye on him.

Owen is restless, however. Harriet tells me about it when I get home.

"He couldn't sit still," she says, "so I took him out shopping."

"Well," I reply, "I'd really prefer him to rest."

The house is now flooded with acrid cigar smoke. I open the windows wide.

The restlessness increases. I am grateful that tomorrow is the day of our clinic appointment.

The psychiatric outpatient clinic of the Long Island Medical Center is located in a small old building behind the new, modern structure. It is clean, quiet. We are the only people in the waiting room.

Dr. Bussoni comes out to greet us. She is young, quite pleasant. I ask if I can speak to her after she sees Owen. She agrees.

"He's doing nicely," she tells me.

"Oh, I'm not so sure," I reply. "He seems to be getting increasingly restless. As his mother, I'm very sensitive to him, and I can feel it."

"Well, I didn't notice it," she says. "He sat quietly and spoke to me. And he was quite rational."

"I'd really feel a lot better if he had some medication. Could you possibly give him a prescription today?"

"For what? Haldol? You know the reaction he had to that."

"Well, maybe a minor tranquilizer, then. Valium or Librium. Anything that will help."

"It's not necessary now. Let's see what happens. Today he is fine."

I am uneasy in the car. Perhaps I am being foolish, I chide myself.

"Would you like to stop by Hollister University?" I suggest. "It's on the way home."

"That's a good idea."

"We'll just have a quick look around. You can see if you like it."

We have lunch in the student union, pick up some bulletins, and leave. Owen is favorably impressed and says he will definitely consider this university when he is ready to return to school. Neither of us knows yet when this will be.

That evening, the restlessness increases. He tells his little brother that Vincent and I are going to get a divorce. I find out about this later.

Suzy is a tremendous helper at this time. She cooks the dinners, since I usually don't get home from work until late, and keeps a protective eye on Owen. They are still very close.

On Wednesday evening, as the red ball of a sun is lowering on the horizon, Owen calls his sister over to the picture window.

"The Russians have just dropped the Bomb," he informs her.

Suzy relays this information to me. I am alarmed at this delusion, but I try not to show it.

"Owen," I tell him, "you know, the Russians wouldn't drop a bomb. No one wants to start World War Three. That would be a terrible thing," I try to reason. "All that you saw was the sun going down."

He smiles. Strangely.

On Thursday, the restlessness increases, worsens. He becomes agitated, frenzied. By the time Vincent arrives home, late that evening, Owen is stalking back and forth like a wild animal. His eyebrows are knotted demonically, his face contorted in anger. Back and forth he goes, around the large living room, as Vincent and I cower.

He turns on us, finally, stalks toward us, pointing his finger threateningly. "I warn you! I may become violent!"

I cringe. In terror. For I have seen that look before. Those eyes before. They are shining brightly.

Vincent and I turn toward each other. We both remember.

Owen has become so agitated that, at 11:45 P.M., we take him back to Psych E-R.

A young female psychiatrist, Dr. Velequez, interviews Owen. She calls us in afterward.

"He's okay," she tells us.

"Doctor," I protest, "he is not okay. He's getting sick again. He's seeing strange things—he's agitated—and he's even threatened us with violence."

"He's really okay," she insists. "He was just a little upset tonight."

"I want him to have medication," I say. "You must give him something to prevent a relapse."

"Yes," Vincent says. "My wife has a good point. We'd like you to give him something tonight."

"Well," she reluctantly says, "we have a choice here with the medication. We can either give him Dalmane, a sleeping pill, or Thorazine, a major tranquilizer. Frankly, I'd rather see him get the Dalmane. It will quiet him, put him to sleep."

"But if he's having a relapse," I protest, "what good will a sleeping pill be? No. He *must* get the Thorazine."

"Very well," she says, evidently displeased by our insistence. "We will give him an injection here—twenty-five milligrams of Thorazine. I will also give you two pills, twenty-five milligrams each, to give to him in the morning. Then I'd like you to take him back to the clinic tomorrow to see Dr. Bussoni. She will be able to give you a prescription, if needed."

The doctor then instructs the male nurse on duty (he is big, bald, and looks like a bouncer in a nightclub) on the medication. He gruffly calls Owen into one of the examining rooms for the shot.

Owen is subdued when we arrive home. It is now 1 A.M. He goes directly to bed and sleeps very soundly.

I do not.

13

NIGHTMARE REVISITED

He is okay . . . That is what the doctor said. But she is wrong. He is not okay. I know it by his speech. By the way he acts. By his eyes . . .

I bring Owen one pill instead of two. For some reason, I am afraid to give him too strong a dose of medication. I will wait until after I see the doctor at the clinic.

It is now Friday morning. Southern sun floods his room, benevolently bathing it in a soft golden glow. He is seated at the edge of his bed. Intense. Mute.

"Good morning," I chirp, merrily. "It's a beautiful day today."

No response.

"I've brought you a pill. The doctor says it will make you feel better." He mechanically takes the pill, swallows it.

"I'm calling the clinic now. We're going back to see Dr. Bussoni this morning."

No response.

The clinic secretary gives us an eleven o'clock appointment. I immediately telephone Dr. Sand.

"He's had a setback," I tell him. "Last night. He became highly agitated and we had to take him back to Psych E-R for medication. They gave him a shot of Thorazine and I've just given him a pill this morning. Doctor, he's not quite right, and I don't know what to do. I'm afraid."

"Well," he says, "I'll have to speak to Dr. Bussoni after she sees Owen. Then, we will decide on a course of action together."

I am not encouraged. He has said absolutely nothing.

Dr. Bussoni walks out with Owen. "He's okay," she tells me.

"Doctor, I'd like to speak with you alone for a minute. May I?"

"Of course."

We go into her office. Owen waits outside.

"He's not okay. There are signs."

She looks at me, quizzically. "He is talking rationally."

"No, he is getting ill again. I want a prescription for Thorazine."

"Very well, I will give you a prescription and I will call Owen in to discuss it."

"Oh—better make it for the generic drug, chlorpromazine," I add. "It will be less expensive."

She writes out the prescription and then calls Owen in.

"I am giving you a prescription for Thorazine—twenty-five-milligram tablets. I want you to have a total of one hundred milligrams a day, taken as follows: one in the morning, one before dinner, and two when you go to sleep. That should be enough to keep you feeling fine."

I reach out for the prescription. The doctor pulls it away from me.

"Oh, no," she says. She hands the prescription to Owen. "I want *him* to be responsible for his own medication."

But—how can he be responsible when he is getting sicker and sicker? I look, incredulous, at the young doctor as Owen crumples the prescription and stuffs it into his pocket.

It is my day off today, this clinic day, and I am happy to be home, for it means that I can keep a close watch on Owen. He must be observed and given the correct number of pills, which we have just purchased.

We spend an uneventful day at home. Owen appears to be rested, rational now. He stays in his room, listening to the Beatles. He is quiet. Unusually quiet. I attribute this to the Thorazine. It has certainly relaxed me, considerably.

Since it is Friday, Vincent is home early. We all have a pleasant dinner together.

"I'm going out tonight with my friends," Suzy declares. "I won't be home till late."

"Okay," I tell her. "We won't double-lock the door."

She leaves a little after nine o'clock.

Vincent and I, exhausted from last night's stint in Psych E-R, decide to retire early.

"I'm beat," he says. "Why don't you give him his medicine so that we can all get a good night's sleep."

"Yes," I reply. "He seems as weary as we are. The pills should put him out like a light."

At 9:30 P.M. I softly enter the boys' bedroom. Tim has just fallen asleep. Owen is seated on the edge of his bed in his pajamas. He appears to be morose. I tell myself that it is simply a combination of fatigue and medication.

"Dad and I are very tired," I tell him. "I'm sure you must be, too. We were up so very late last night. Here's your medication. Please take these two pills now and go to sleep." He swallows the pills and lies down. I shut the door behind me.

Hours later we are both awakened by strange, maniacal laughter. Voices raised in lively conversation. Who is having a party? Half-asleep, I glance at the digital clock. It is 1 A.M. Vincent gets up to investigate.

It must be Owen. He seems to be having a cheerful conversation with someone. But who? Who would visit him, unannounced, at this hour? And why would someone be here anyway, since I said good-night to him hours ago. He went to bed at nine-thirty. Or did he? . . .

I put my bathrobe on and peek into the living room. Vince is conversing, quite earnestly, with a young fellow whom I recognize. But from where? My sleepy brain is slow to function. Of course, he had worked with Owen at the local supermarket. It's Bart. But what is he doing here now? In the middle of the night. And where is Owen? I look around, but he is nowhere in sight. Strange . . . I glance again into the living room. Bart is handing several small objects to Vincent. I cannot make out what they are. They whisper. Faces serious. I retreat into my bedroom. When I hear our "guest" leave, a short while later, I come out into the living room. Vincent's face has turned ashen.

"What's the matter? What was he doing here at this hour?"

"You won't believe what happened."

"I will believe almost anything now. Try me."

"Well," he explains, "Owen got up, about midnight, crept down the stairs and out—in his pajamas and bare feet, mind you —and walked across Main Street and went into the local pub, Harvie's Hideaway, where all the kids hang out. He went in, asking for a beer, and fortunately, Bart spotted him and brought him home. Can you imagine that? In pajamas and bare feet! It must be thirty degrees out there tonight."

"My God!"

"Oh, that isn't the best part. I'm getting to that, now. Your son had these things in his hand, which he showed to Bart. Bart took them away from him."

Vincent opens his clenched fist, producing a razor and a bottle of Librium. My unused Librium. I shake my head in disbelief as Vince continues, in a low monotone.

" 'He was high on something, Mr. Etons' is what Bart said."

High on something . . . Still . . .

Neither one of us can say anything now. Vince stands motionless, clutching the razor and the Librium.

"Where did Owen go?" I ask him.

"I don't know. He just left the room when I came in."

We find him in the bathroom. Seated on the tub. A previously unopened bottle of syrup of ipecac stands on the sink. Empty. Owen has obviously drunk it! We confront him. Speechless. Vincent places the razor and the partially emptied bottle of Librium on the sink, next to the empty bottle of ipecac.

"He's drunk it!" I say. "The whole bottle!"

Owen stares at us. Silent. His eyes glimmer. Silver. Rosemary's Baby's eyes.

"We have an emergency," I whisper to Vince. "He's taken Librium, I don't know how many, a whole bottle of ipecac, and the Thorazine, too!"

"We'll have to get him back to Psych E-R," Vince says. "We better not waste any time."

We get dressed quickly and then help Owen on with his clothes. Suzy comes home as we are about to leave.

"I'm so glad you're home. Stay with Tim. Owen's had a relapse. We're taking him back to the hospital."

"Yes," Suzy says, "I knew it was happening." The sweet smile of greeting fades. She goes directly to her room, for she cannot bear to see her brother like this. They have always been so close.

We get Owen outside and into the car. It is now 1:30 A.M. and the streets are relatively empty. I speed, frantically, on the highway, almost hoping for a police chase, for I now have a medical emergency on my hands. I only slacken my speed as I see the twinkling rooftop lights of that beckoning edifice, the Long Island Medical Center.

Once safely inside Psych E-R, I relate Owen's evening activities to the nurse on duty.

"Librium and ipecac," she repeats. "How many Librium did he take?"

"I don't know."

"And what about the ipecac? Are you sure he drank it all?"

"Yes. The bottle had never been used. And," I remind her, "don't forget the Thorazine. He had two at nine-thirty."

"In this case," she informs us, "he doesn't belong here. Not yet. We have to get him right over to the medical E-R."

An orderly escorts us down the main hall to the medical E-R.

We meet the young doctor on duty. I repeat the unsavory combination of drugs that Owen has ingested.

"We'll have to keep him here for a while and watch him very closely. We'll be questioning him, too," he adds.

Questioning him? That seems a rather silly thing to do to someone who isn't rational.

For some reason, they do not pump his stomach. I wonder why.

Vincent and I are forced to wait, in the outside corridor, for well over an hour. Then Owen is escorted by the orderly, with us in close pursuit, back to Psych E-R.

Again he must wait to be interviewed by the psychiatrist on duty.

Again it is a young woman doctor.

She calls us in afterward, asking Owen to wait outside. "Well," she says, matter-of-factly, "he seems to have had a relapse. He is clearly in a psychotic state and must be hospitalized again."

A psychotic state . . . How can you tell? I want to ask. I am momentarily speechless with the horror of it all.

"Look," I say, "two psychiatrists here in the last two days said he was okay. Okay. Can you believe that?"

"Well," she hedges, "he was probably okay when they saw him."

"No," I reply firmly, my voice rising. "He was not okay at all. He was getting sicker and sicker, and no one would believe me. I saw it. My daughter saw it. And no one would believe me!"

"Let's not discuss this now, Ursula," Vincent interrupts. "It's not going to improve the situation."

"I am sorry," I tell him later, in private, "but I am appalled at the ineptitude of the medical profession."

We wait once more in Psych E-R. We wait and wait through the long night. It almost seems that we are spending the better part of our lives in this lower level of hell.

The night dies. And with it, our spirits. It is now nearly dawn. Owen is fatigued by his ordeal. He goes into one of the small cubicles to lie down. When I go in to check on him, several minutes later, I find him lying there, staring at the ceiling. In tears. It seems as if, in the back of his disoriented mind, he knows. He knows what the angel dust has done. And he is sorry.

Don't cry, my sweet prince . . . I lean over him and kiss him lightly on the forehead. "It will be all right," I sob, "It will be all right." For nearly four weeks now I have been telling myself it will be all right . . .

At five in the morning, Owen Etons, age nineteen, is readmitted to the psychiatric division of the Long Island Medical Center. He is sent, at my urgent request, to the open ward on the twelfth floor. Two large security guards lead him away.

14

RETURN OF THE ZOMBIES

"I want to find out how my son is doing. Owen Etons. He was admitted at five this morning."

"He isn't here," the nurse on duty says.

"But he was taken up to O-P last night."

"We had to transfer him back down to Ten," she says. "He was uncontrollable."

Ward 10 again. It is clearly a setback. But, considering his bizarre behavior of the previous night, I am not too surprised.

"Yes, Owen came in about eight this morning," Mrs. Coates, the head day nurse, tells me.

"How is he doing?"

"Still pretty difficult. Quite violent at the moment."

Violent. Owen. "Is he on medication, I hope?"

"We can't get any medication to stay down. He's been vomiting all morning."

"My God. It must be the ipecac."

"Probably. Anyway, we'll have to wait until he stops vomiting before we can administer anything."

"Has the doctor seen him?"

"The chief psychiatrist, Dr. Ressler, has. A little while ago."

"What about Dr. Sand? I want him on the case again."

"Well, you'll have to speak to Dr. Ressler about that. Dr. Sand may be leaving psychiatry shortly. I think he's due back on the neurology rotation."

This bit of unexpected news distresses me. Dr. Sand is the only positive thing going for us at this hospital. I call the office of the chief psychiatrist. He is not in. I leave a message with his secretary, that I want Dr. Sand back on the case.

In the afternoon, I again telephone 10. The nurse on duty hardly cheers my spirits. Owen has been vomiting continuously. He cannot retain any medication. For him, for his illness, the day is lost.

"He's being kept in an isolation room, right next to the nurses' station," I am informed. This is, ostensibly, for his own protection, as well as for the protection of others. But, it is more likely, for the convenience of the nurses.

"How is he acting now?" I want to know.

"He's still quite violent. He's been ripping up his bedding, pulling off his hospital clothes, and tearing pictures off the wall. That's why we've had to isolate him."

"Say no more," I respond. "I'll be there tonight."

In the evening, Vincent and I make a brief visit to the hospital. We wait an unbearably long time for Owen to come out. As we sit, the walk of the zombies begins. One by one, clad in hospital white, they materialize. Gliding, eyes staring blankly ahead, they march into the room. The faces are strange, but the march never changes.

Owen finally appears, wearing hospital gown and trousers. Upon entering the room, he turns from us, walks directly to the bulletin board hanging on the wall, and begins to rip the colorful posters off it, tossing them on the floor.

"Stop!" I jump up and pull him down on the sofa between us.

He now becomes sullen, mumbling incoherently. After only a few brief minutes, he rises, like a zombie-ghost, and walks back inside the ward. Tonight, he has rejected the Real World. Vince and I are left seated. Alone.

On Sunday morning I telephone the hospital and speak to the nurse on duty. "How is Owen doing this morning?"

"Well, he's about the same."

"The same? What do you mean?"

"He was pretty violent last night when I came on duty."

"What about the vomiting? Has it stopped?"

"Oh, yes. He's not vomiting any more."

"And the medication? He must be getting something now. What is it?"

"He's on Thorazine now, because of the bad reaction he had with the Haldol. But I'm not supposed to discuss the dosage. You'll have to ask the doctor about that."

"Very good. I'll be there this afternoon."

At one in the afternoon, Vincent, Suzy, and I arrive at Ward 10 for the visiting hour. Again we wait an uncomfortably long time for Owen to come out.

He appears in the doorway, sheathed in white. I go over and greet him. He makes no reply, but he does appear to recognize Suzy. She gives him a warm hug.

We all try to converse with him, but to no avail. He is sullen, uncommunicative. Occasionally he utters a rational phrase, but for the most part he is incoherent.

Before the visiting hour is over, he gets up, in silence, and walks back, my white zombie, to the inner ward. The safe, Absurd World.

"I have got to speak with Dr. Sand," I say to the secretary. It is now Monday morning.

"I will leave a message. He is not in Neurology now. This is a big hospital, you know."

I know. Only too well.

Patience has never been my major virtue. I keep calling the hospital. Neurology, Psychiatry, the open ward, Ward 10. Dr. Sand is not to be found. It is impossible for me to concentrate on my job. My son is ill. Violent. Irrational. And I don't even know who's helping him.

Mid-afternoon. The phone rings on my desk. It is Dr. Sand.

"I've been trying frantically to reach you! All day, in fact!" I blurt out.

"I know. I've just seen Owen."

"How is he?"

"Right now he's completely uncommunicative."

"Why, doctor? Why did he have this relapse?"

"I don't know. Nobody knows."

"But don't you see, I felt it would happen. That's why I didn't want him taken off the Haldol. Don't you see?"

"Mrs. Etons, believe me, no one could have anticipated this."

"What's being done for him now?"

"We've put him on Thorazine. It's just as effective as Haldol and there are fewer side effects. I've just increased the dosage to four hundred milligrams a day."

"I assume, doctor, that you've been assigned to Owen, at my request."

"Yes, I have. At least for a while. I'll soon be transferring out of Psychiatry and back to my own department."

"I see. Well, I hope that doesn't happen until Owen's well again."

In the evening, Vince and I arrive at Ward 10 for the appointed visiting hour. We witness the walk of the zombies. But Owen does not appear. Finally, after waiting about twenty minutes, the nurse on duty comes over to us. Her face is unusually serious.

"I'm so sorry," she explains, "but your son is simply too agitated tonight to come out. If you would like to see him, I can arrange for him to be brought into a room in the women's ward and you can go in there for a few minutes."

"The women's ward?" I ask. "Is there any reason why we can't come into his room in the men's ward?"

"Well, we have quite a few violent patients in there at the moment. It will be safest for you in the women's ward."

"Fine," Vince says. "We want to see him."

She leads us into the inner sanctum, through double doors, down a long narrow corridor, and into a small private room.

Owen arrives in a short while, escorted by a male orderly. He looks simply awful. Hair unkempt, face flushed, eyes glazed. He appears to be in a state of utter panic.

"Hi, Owen," I say. He mumbles unintelligibly.

"Here, Owen, we've brought you a milk shake." He takes the milk shake from me and slowly sips half of it. Then he goes over to the bed and lies down on his back. His eyes are filled with tears.

"It's okay," I comfort him. "Everything will be okay now. Dr. Sand is taking care of you again, and you are getting new medicine which will make you better."

He rolls over on his stomach and I begin to massage his shouders. After several minutes of this steady massaging, his body seems to relax.

"How are you feeling?" Vince asks. He mumbles incoherently. Vince sits down in a chair in a corner of the room.

I continue with the gentle massaging. I do not know how else to comfort my sick child. Words are now strange sounds to him. Suspect. But physical contact seems to do wonders, for in a very short while, he closes his eyes and appears to be dozing off.

The nurse enters the room. "I'm afraid he'll have to go back to his room now."

"But," I protest, "he's so much more relaxed now. Please let us stay with him for a little while longer."

"I'm sorry," she insists, "but you're not supposed to be in here at all. And I only promised that you could see him for a few minutes. He's just not well enough to sustain a longer visit."

The orderly comes over to the bed with her and they both get Owen to his feet. I watch, helplessly, as they lead him down the long corridor to the male ward.

The next morning, I call Ward 10 and speak to the head nurse. My usual procedure, early each day.

"How is Owen doing?" I ask.

"He's about the same." She will offer no further information.

I arrive for the early afternoon visiting hour. Again I must wait and watch the zombies. They all glide in and sit, most of them silently, with their visitors.

There is no sign of Owen. It is nearly one-twenty.

Finally, the day nurse approaches me.

"He's not well enough to come out to see you," she says.

"But he was so sick last night. I've got to see him."

"Well, in that case I will let you come into his room for a few minutes. But I must advise you in advance that he is still in isolation, for his own protection and that of the other patients."

"I understand," I reply.

She leads me through the double doors and down the long corridor to the male wing. Just past the nurses' station there is a locked door. She opens it slowly and I peer in.

The sight that confronts me nearly defies description. It is as if I am transported back to Victorian England, to an insane asylum in London, circa 1890. A young man is lying on a rubber mat on the floor (there is no bedding on it), garbed only in a hospital gown. Harsh northern light glares into his eyes through a large locked window. His glazed eyes stare, blankly, at the ceiling. There is no air in the room. Only dry, parching heat.

I bend down and pull Owen up to his feet, opening the heavy door to get fresh air into that stuffy room.

"Owen—it's all right. I'm here. I'm here to take care of you. Look, I've brought you a malted. Your mouth is so dry—take a sip." I hand him the malted. He gulps it down quickly.

"Now, we've got to get out of this room. Come, let's take a little walk." I put my arm around him and, dazed though he is, I manage to get him out into the corridor.

I walk him up and down the long corridor. Up and down. To clear the fogged mind. Up and down. To move the dormant body. Up and down. To get the blood flowing again to his once splendid brain.

Dr. Ressler is now at the nurses' station. I sit Owen down on the floor and lean him against the corridor wall, cautioning him to wait there, and walk over to speak to the doctor.

"Can you get him out of that awful room?" I plead. "Or at least let him have a regular bed."

"No," he informs me. "He will fall out of a regular bed."

"But how can someone get well in that kind of an atmosphere?"

"Look, Mrs. Etons, if you are dissatisfied with our facilities, you can always transfer your son to a private hospital."

"To be perfectly honest with you," I admit, "I have thought of that. I do not want to transfer him when he is this sick, but perhaps you could give me the names of some private hospitals here on Long Island—in case I need one in the future."

Dr. Ressler jots down the names of a half-dozen hospitals in my area and hands me the list. I thank him and go back to Owen.

"Let's go and find the dayroom now," I say, helping Owen to his feet. "There must be a dayroom here." We walk to the end of the corridor and, sure enough, at the very end, there is a fairly large dayroom. It isn't as modern or plush as the one in Ward O-P. The floors are bare, the furniture old and wooden, and the TV set is located here, not in a separate area. There are, as in Ward O-P, games, magazines, and an old phonograph. I pick up an issue of *Time*, sit Owen down in a chair, and place the magazine in front of him on the table. He turns the pages briefly and then jumps up and starts walking about, aimlessly.

"Okay," I say, "I guess you want to walk some more." Again we go out into the corridor and walk. Up and down. Up and down.

The nurse comes over to us. "Well, he looks like he's doing better," she says. "Look, Mrs. Etons, I've let you stay here, where you're not supposed to be, and now visiting hours are over. You'll really have to go."

"I understand," I reply. "Please let me walk Owen back into the dayroom. That isolation room is much too hot. There's no ventilation at all."

"Well, I'll go and put on the air conditioning for a little while," she offers. "That should help."

I walk Owen back into the dayroom. More patients have entered. It is a strange place, pervaded by an atmosphere of unreality. Here patients sit on the floor—one is even sleeping on top of a table—and they mutter and mumble. And nobody notices. They are all, it seems, in the throes of deep psychoses.

"Here." I sit Owen down at one of the empty tables. "I want

you to stay here for a while and read." Then you can go back
to your room and rest." I place another magazine, *Hot Rod*
(because he likes cars), in front of him and walk to the door,
glancing back to make sure he is still seated. He is. But I
know it won't be for long.

That afternoon I call Hilldale, the most prominent private
hospital in Marsey County, one which has a separate center for
mental patients and an excellent world-renowned medical staff.

"I'm sorry," I am told, "but if your son is in a locked ward,
we cannot accept him."

I wait until evening and then discuss the situation with Vincent. He listens to my vivid description of my journey back
through time, my futile effort to pull Owen out of his trance-
like state, and then my tale of the rejection by Hilldale Hospital. He can offer no consolation.

"We'll just have to leave him where he is. We certainly can't
bring him home."

"I realize we can't bring him home, but I'm still very distressed at what I saw." I consider immediately calling the other
private hospitals on the list but then decide that they, too, may
refuse Owen admission. And one rejection per day is enough.
We are stuck, for the time being, with the medical center.

It is now Wednesday morning. I make my routine call to
Ward 10. And I get my routine answer. "He is about the same."

Dr. Sand phones me in the afternoon, as is now his practice
during the week.

"I see a slight improvement today," he says.

"Is he rational yet?"

"No. We can't say that he's rational yet. But the drug appears
to be taking effect. We're increasing the dosage gradually,
each day."

We visit Owen in the evening. After only a short wait, he
comes out to the visitors' room. The zombies have been rejected.
He is wearing street clothes. Just these observations alone are
enough to convince me that he is, indeed, improving.

Basically, he remains uncommunicative. But, at times, he is able to utter rational statements. And he sits, quietly, between Vince and me, through most of the visit. We are both elated just to have him here, in the social context of the visitors' room.

"Tomorrow is Thanksgiving," I mention to Vince as we get into the car. "I hope you weren't expecting me to make a turkey."

Thanksgiving. Always a joyous occasion, it is now a sad time for our family. Vince prods me. I have no desire to eat out. But I must, he tells me, think of the younger children.

He orders the traditional dinner for all of us and I ask the waitress, when we are done, to make up a nice thick turkey sandwich for my son. We bring it to the hospital.

Marc and Marsha, in for the holiday, are waiting for us outside Ward 10. The door is unbolted and I go in with Marc. After a few minutes, Owen appears.

"Hi Owen. Look, I've brought you a turkey sandwich. Today is Thanksgiving." He takes the sandwich from me and munches it rapidly, mumbling incoherently all the while. His mouth is stuffed as he mutters; it is impossible to understand him.

He sits there between us, dressed, but unkempt. Totally irrational. I feel saddened by the fact that the other children have to see him like this.

In the evening, Vince and I go back to the hospital (visiting is allowed twice a day on holidays). Owen is led out by a nurse. He appears to be half-asleep and, evidently, we have awakened him by our visit.

Although he is out of touch with the Real World, he is trying, desperately, to get back in. He walks around, from visitor to visitor, asking the same question. "Where am I? Where am I? Am I on Mars?" He giggles. "Am I on the Earth?" He smiles.

"Of course you're on the Earth," I assure him, leading him over to the sofa. I am embarrassed. But why? All of the patients here are very sick. But most of them are silent.

Owen looks at me. Seriously. "I am dead," he states.

I suppose that he is dead, in a sense. The real Owen is not in existence at this time. I understand what he is saying. Only too well.

He gets up again. The sleepiness is gone and the restlessness returns. He walks about the room, then climbs up on an end table, pauses briefly, and jumps off. Vincent is now embarrassed. He tries to get Owen to sit still. Impossible.

"I'm getting there. I'm getting there," Owen repeats. Then he mumbles incoherently.

On Friday morning I make my routine call to 10. One of my favorite day nurses answers. "I see some improvement," she says. "However, he is still restless and I had to stay with him to get him to eat his breakfast." I am heartened by this news.

Since it is Thanksgiving weekend, Dr. Sand is off and Owen is seen by a substitute doctor. I speak with him on the phone and he informs me that he has increased the dosage of Thorazine to six hundred fifty milligrams. This is even more encouraging.

Tonight we can see some improvement. Owen appears rather serious, yet rational. He converses on a very limited basis. We have to initiate the conversation, but what he says makes sense.

"I want to get better," he tells us.

"You're doing just fine," Vince says.

"But my hands are shaking," he notes.

"It's nothing," I tell him. "There shouldn't be any side effects from the drug they're giving you now."

"What's the name of the drug?" he wants to know.

"It's Thorazine," I say.

He sits quietly now. The jumbled chemicals in his brain, scattered like the pieces of a jigsaw puzzle, are coming back into place. It is a remarkable sight to behold.

After forty-five pleasant minutes, Owen gets up. "I think I'll go inside now," he says. It seems difficult for him to spend the entire hour with us. But, I note, the other young patients all seem to have the same problem. They are all rather uncomfortable with their parents.

"Get a good night's sleep," Vince says, patting him on the back.

"Is there anything you want me to bring you tomorrow?" I ask.

"Yes," he replies. "I'd like my glasses."

I kiss him good-night and we walk out, happily. The Thorazine is definitely working. And tonight, I will be able to sleep once more.

On Saturday the visiting hour is a totally agreeable one. Suzy has come to the hospital with me. Owen is very pleased to see her.

"How are you feeling today?" I ask.

"Much better" is the reply. He is in a pleasant, more talkative mood. "Were you able to bring my glasses?"

"Yes. Here—put them on. I'll ask the nurse if I can leave them with you." He puts them on and smiles.

"You're wearing a new outfit," he says to me.

"Yes." I am pleased that he notices. He is once more becoming outer-directed.

"Here," Suzy says, "we brought you some pictures of hi-fi sets. We know you want one."

"Great." He takes the colorful brochures from her and studies them. They discuss the various models and he now appears to be completely rational.

At the end of the hour I give him a couple of dimes. "Please call home if you feel like it," I suggest. He puts the coins in his shirt pocket.

Once more it is Sunday. Vincent, Suzy, and I go to the hospital. Owen comes out, dressed, but, quite strangely, in bare feet. It is very cold in the visitors' room. Vincent asks the nurse for a pair of peds and she helps him put them on.

"Where are your glasses?" I ask. His eyes appear to be strained.

"They took them away from me," he replies, sleepily. The powerful dosage of medication is taking its toll.

"Well, perhaps we can get them back for you," Vince says.

We spend the rest of the visit watching him as he jumps up and then sits down again. I wonder once more, is it the medication? Or the illness itself? It is most disconcerting. But, at least I console myself with the fact that today Owen knows precisely where he is.

Dr. Sand is back at the hospital on Monday. We speak on the telephone.

"I still see a borderline psychosis," he says.

"Well, I don't," I reply. "He's perfectly rational."

"Oh, he's much improved," the doctor states, "but he's not quite normal. There is still a looseness of thought and association. Therefore, I am not reducing the dosage of medication."

"I'm glad. I want him to be perfectly well again."

That evening, there is a setback. When Vince and I arrive at the hospital the nurse comes out to see us.

"We've had a reaction to the medication," she says. "They're giving him a shot of Cogentin right now. You'll have to wait a few minutes until he's up to coming out."

Again. They have cured the disease but destroyed the patient.

Owen appears in the doorway. His mouth is stiff and distorted, almost paralyzed. He cannot move his tongue. When he sees us his eyes fill with tears. He is unable to move his twisted mouth. Unable to ask for help. His hands are shaking, and as I help him over to the sofa to sit down, I realize that he appears to be sensitive to large doses of all major tranquilizers. Once more the staff has neglected to administer the counteractive medication. Again they have waited. And again they have been wrong.

"It will be all right," I assure him. "It will be all right. Here, we've brought you a hot chocolate. Try to sip some. It will make you feel better." I hold the container for him but his mouth is far too stiff. It is a few minutes before he is able to slowly sip the rich hot drink.

Within a short while, Owen is asleep, his head resting on the back of the sofa.

Insult is added to injury. A rash has developed. I notice it the next day. It is all over his arms, legs, and the back of his neck. It resembles prickly heat. But it is not. He is quite uncomfortable and cannot stop stratching.

"Please," I beg, "leave it alone. I will bring you some calamine tomorrow."

"Do you think I got this from contact with the other patients?" he asks.

"No," I reply, trying to ignore the seeming paranoia of that question. "It is just another side effect from the Thorazine."

He is smoking, puffing intently.

"I've brought Tim with me today," I tell him. "I'm going to ask the receptionist if he can come in for a minute."

"Fine," Owen replies.

The receptionist agrees. But only for a minute.

Tim is happy to see his brother. He has not seen him since the relapse. I think the visit is beneficial for Owen, too.

"Do you think I'll be going home soon?" Owen asks.

"Well, first you'll be going up to twelve for a while. Then you'll be able to go home."

He quietly accepts that.

When visiting hours end, I go up to the Neurology Department to see Dr. Sand.

"I am very concerned about the rash," he tells me. "This can lead to all kinds of complications internally. I will have to take him off the Thorazine."

"Oh, not again!" I reply.

"He'll be getting Cogentin for the next couple of days, and then, if all is well, we can put him back on either Thorazine or a low dose of Haldol."

"What can I say, doctor? You know I don't like to see him off medication. Especially so soon."

"Now," he changes the subject, "in a few days I will be changing my rotation. I will be leaving Psychiatry and coming back to Neurology. Therefore, I have spoken to Dr. Ressler and he may treat Owen himself."

More miserable news. There is nothing further that I can say.

———

Tonight, as I am preparing dinner, there is a phone call. It is Owen. I am so pleased to hear from him. It is as if all the bad news of the day is totally wiped out. By his voice.

"Hi!" he says. "What's doing?"

The next evening, Wednesday, Vince, Suzy, and I all visit Owen. His spirits have improved and the rash looks lighter. Nevertheless, I have brought calamine and cotton and I apply the soothing lotion to his arms and neck.

"Hey!" the nurse admonishes me. "You're not supposed to give him any kind of medication."

"Well, he's very uncomfortable," I say, "and I want him to feel better." I hand him the bottle and he dabs some lotion on his legs.

The nurse glowers at us. I couldn't care less.

"I've been thinking about college," Owen says. "I'd like to take a look at two other colleges on the Island. As soon as I'm out of here."

"Of course. But remember, you don't have to make up your mind just yet. You won't be going back for the spring semester."

"I know," he answers, sadly.

"Mom and Dad say they're getting you a car." Suzy tries to cheer him.

"Really?" He perks up. "That's great."

"What's your favorite car?" she wants to know.

"Well," he hesitates, "my favorite car is too expensive."

"Tell me anyway," she insists.

"It's the Firebird."

"Mine's the Corvette Stingray," Suzy states.

"You both sound like you're entering the Indianapolis 500," Vince quips.

Visiting hour draws to a close. I wish Owen a good night's sleep.

"I couldn't sleep too well last night," he says. "My head was bothering me."

"Did they give you anything for it?" I ask.

"Yes. I asked for Tylenol and they gave me two."

"Look," I suggest, "if you can't sleep tonight, ask for some Valium."

"I will," he promises, as the nurse announces that visiting hours are over.

"I think you missed your calling," Vince says to me as we get into the car. "You definitely should apply to medical school."

On Thursday afternoon when I visit Owen I am pleased by the progress he is making. He looks so much better, although he still has a slight rash. When the nurse isn't looking, I put a drop more calamine on his arms and neck.

However, he is smoking again. I try not to notice.

"I'm really feeling much better," he assures me.

When I get back to work I call Dr. Sand.

"We did a blood count on him Tuesday," he states. "Because of the rash. The results were normal. No problems there."

"He seems to be doing so much better," I say.

"Yes. He is no longer psychotic."

Funny—I told him that last Friday. "What about medication now?" I ask.

"He'll probably get a small dose of Haldol tomorrow. We haven't made a definite decision on that as yet."

"I see."

"By the way, as I mentioned to you a few days ago, I will be leaving Psychiatry this week and Owen will be assigned to a new doctor. Her name is Dr. Arbo. She is a neurologist. I'm sure you'll like her."

"Doctor," I reply, "I like you. I am not happy about this change at all."

In the evening, at 8 P.M., I receive a phone call. I am at work.

"Hi, Mother," Owen says. "I just called home and Tim told me you were at work. He gave me the number. I just called to say hello."

"What a nice thought," I tell him.

The pieces of the puzzle are definitely falling into place.

On Friday, December second, the head nurse informs me that Owen will be transferred back up to O-P.

"He'll be taken up right after supper."

"Fine," I tell her. "I will be there."

At 6 P.M. I arrive at Ward 10. Calling in, I immediately get a positive response. I am no longer a stranger on the intercom. "I will be right out," the head nurse informs me. A few minutes later she is in the corridor, pointing. "He will be coming out through those doors," she says, "in about ten minutes." I wait in the corridor, seated on a cold radiator. This is truly a momentous occasion. Owen is being transferred, at long last, to the respectable open ward, O-P.

A few minutes later, the door opens, and Owen is escorted out, along with another young male patient, by two security guards and a female work-clerk. I latch on to the group and we ride up to O-P together.

Our ordeal, in 10, is now over.

A new one is yet to begin. . . .

15

THE ROAD TO NOWHERE

Ward 10 is behind us now. The vomiting. The violence. The pale, steady stream of zombies. All of the painful things are fading into the past. But we still have a battle ahead. And at this time I am not aware of how difficult it is still going to be.

One thing is certain, however. The handwriting is on the wall. We have to get Owen out of the Long Island Medical Center. But where do we take him? And when?

I ponder these questions while at work. It is Saturday and I won't be able to visit the hospital until evening. As I sit, immobilized by indecision, the telephone rings. It is Owen.

"How are you feeling today?" I ask him.

"Just fine. Still have a little rash, though. They're not giving me any medication because of it."

"I see." This fact disturbs me but I cannot say anything to him.

"Would you believe they've put me back in the old room?"

"Well, that's splendid. Do you have the same roommates?"

"No. The other guys left. But the new guys seem pretty nice. Are you coming this afternoon?"

"No. I have a few appointments here. Dad will be there this afternoon. I won't be able to make it until tonight. Can I bring you anything?"

"Yeah. Cigars. Muriel Air Tips, if possible."

"Sure. See you later."

Cigars. The smoking has intensified. Indeed, most of the patients there are heavy smokers. And in an atmosphere like that,
it is difficult to refrain. Yes, I will bring little cigars to him.
Every day.

That evening, directly after work, I visit Owen for two hours.
When I enter the main corridor, I find him playing Ping-Pong
with one of the other young male patients. I greet him and go
into the dayroom to put down my coat.

Patients are quietly sitting in groups of twos and threes, talking, playing cards, reading. Except for Serita. Serita has been
here for many weeks. "She is a schizophrenic," one of the
patients has told me. Serita is always alone. Always attired in
bathrobe and slippers. Always smoking and pacing back and
forth, in the corridor and dayroom. And she mumbles to herself,
waving her arms about, as she goes. She is a pretty, young
woman, terribly thin, with long black hair and milky white skin.
Tonight Serita approaches me as I place my coat on the back of
one of the chairs.

"I am Serita," she says. "What's your name?"

"Ursula," I reply.

"You are so beautiful." She touches my face.

"Why, thank you." I am embarrassed.

"Do you like me?"

"Yes. Of course I like you," I assure her. "You're very pretty,
too."

"Oh," she looks relieved. "I have to give you a kiss." She
kisses me lightly on the cheek. "Say," she remembers, "do you
have a match?" She produces a cigarette.

"Oh, sure," I reply. "Here, let me light that for you."

"Thanks." She takes a long drag. "Thanks." And this ethereal
young woman glides off, shuffling her slippered feet, and mumbling incoherently as she goes.

Owen comes into the dayroom and sits opposite me at a table
near the window. I hand him two packs of cigars.

"I got some of these today," he tells me.

"Where?"

"I went outside with Bob, the guy you saw me playing Ping-Pong with."

"How did you manage that?"

"They gave me privileges. For good behavior, I guess."

"Where did you go?"

"To that little tobacco shop across the street."

"Owen! That's across the highway. I don't think you should have done that."

"Oh, well, Bob was with me. Don't worry. I'm all right."

"Yes. But please don't go off hospital grounds again."

He puffs on his cigar, then looks at me intently. "Look," he says, "I want to get out of this place. I want to come home. Now."

"I know, but we have to wait a little longer."

"Why?"

"Well, I have to speak to your new doctor on Monday. Then I'll have more to tell you. In the meantime, I'm going to talk to the nurse tonight to find out why you're not getting any medication."

"It's the rash," he says, laughing rather strangely. I look at him. He is engulfed by cigar smoke.

"Look, Owen, here's tonight's *Newsday*. You read it while I go out to the nurses' station."

Out in the corridor, just a few yards in front of the nurses' station, a huge black man is yelling. "I wanna get out of this place!" He looks like a young Joe Lewis.

The night nurse whispers to me, "You'd better go back into the dayroom. There's going to be trouble here."

I back into the dayroom and stand looking through the glass partition. The nurse's warning was justified. A genuine fracas has developed.

The man has now become violent, thrashing his arms wildly and screaming, "I'm gettin' out of this place! No one's gonna stop me!"

He pushes the two male orderlies about, and starts to punch, savagely, with both fists. Three security guards come rushing in, there is a wild scuffle, and then, finally, they drag him off, down the corridor, presumably to his room. The head nurse comes running after them with a syringe in her hand.

As I stand in the doorway now, I hear the nurses' aide phoning down to Ward 10 to arrange his transfer there. He is too violent for O-P. They will have none of it. As she completes the call, one of the orderlies comes dashing back down the corridor with a straightjacket in his hands.

I glance back at Owen. He is calmly reading the newspaper.

The nurse confirms what we already know. Owen is on no medication at the moment. She suggests that I speak to his new doctor on Monday.

"Monday. That means that we are losing two more days."

"I know," she replies. "But there's nothing I can do."

"And the weekend resident? Will it help if I speak to him?"

"I doubt it. Owen seems to be okay."

Okay . . . I am sick of that meaningless word.

"Well," I tell Owen, "I will definitely have to speak to the doctor on Monday. I'm sure it won't be much longer."

"It better not be."

"Look, I may not be able to come twice a day, but I will see you every day. You can be sure of that."

"Good. And please bring cigars every day. Two packs, if you don't mind."

I clear away the smoke with my hand. "Of course," I reply.

Harry, the dog-man, has now spotted the smoke. He comes over to our table, barking ferociously.

"Arf-arf!" Harry barks, extending his hand for a cigarette.

"No, Harry," Owen says. "I don't have any cigarettes. These are cigars. They're very bad for your health."

On Sunday, Vince and I visit the hospital together.

"I'm bringing up the subject of a transfer," I tell him as we ride up in the elevator.

"Do you think it's wise to mention it before we have any definite placement for him?"

"I have to prepare him," I insist. "Especially since he wants to come home."

Owen is waiting for us in the twelfth-floor lobby. He is neatly dressed, combed, and looks well, physically.

"Why, your rash looks just about gone," I tell him.

"Yeah. I've given up the pastime of scratching."

We sit down in the dayroom and I bring up the subject of a transfer.

"Owen, this week I'm going to try to get you into a private hospital here on Long Island."

"What's wrong with this one?" he wants to know.

"I don't think you're getting enough personal attention here. Also, I'd like to see you back on medication. That's why I think a private hospital is a better idea."

"Well, I'm not too keen on leaving here just to go someplace else. I know everyone here."

"Well, you'll make friends in another place. You've always made friends easily."

"What about coming home? That's what I really want to do."

"Well, it would be best for you to have a little more treatment. Just to be on the safe side."

He shakes his head, totally unconvinced. I do not pursue the subject any further.

Vince gets him to read the Sunday newspapers. Owen glances, dutifully, at them. He is not yet able to concentrate. They discuss sports. It is Vincent's favorite subject.

"Look at Catfish Hunter. He's a three-million dollar disappointment. What do you think Willie Mays would make in today's market?"

Owen is silent. It is now difficult for him to calculate.

"Come on," Vincent prods, "give it a try."

"Well," Owen responds, "I guess somewhere between five and ten million. Easily."

Vince is satisfied. And so am I. I know very little about baseball but I am pleased that Owen is able to give this subject some rational thought.

Owen talks politics with me.

"Connally will run for president in 1980," he says.

"How do you know?"

"I know. He happens to be a great man."

"But I thought you were a Democrat," I remind him.

"I am. But I still think Connally will make a good president."

And, as he now glances through the Sunday *Times*, strange ideas come into focus. He is still tremendously worried about the Russians. About atomic warfare.

"There's going to be another war," he says, grimly. "The Russians are ready."

"No need for concern," Vince replies.

"But don't you see?" he continues. "It's got to start in the Middle East. And the Russians will instigate it. They have the Bomb."

On Monday morning, I telephone two private hospitals in Marsey County. The first one is the world-renowned hospital, Hilldale, which had refused to take Owen from the locked ward. Now that he is in an open ward again, I feel certain that they will admit him. I speak to the social worker.

"I will have to call the medical center and see what your son's condition is now," he informs me. "I will get back to you shortly."

A few minutes later, he phones me back.

"I spoke to your son's doctor," he says. "At the moment they are trying to stabilize him and find a suitable medication."

"I see." I assume he means they are trying to find something that does not produce side effects. "But I'd really much rather have him treated at your hospital. Can I bring him in this week?"

"I'd like to say yes, but unfortunately we are filled up at the moment. There's a two-week wait."

In desperation, I phone another private hospital, one without any reputation at all, but close to my home. No, they also reply, they do not have a psychiatric bed available at this time.

What to do? As Vince would put it, sit tight. What choice do I have.

Owen's new doctor, Dr. Arbo, telephones me at work.

"We'll be putting him on a minute dosage of Haldol tomorrow," she says. "One milligram, twice a day."

"That hardly sounds like anything at all," I comment.

"Well, at the moment, that will be the safest way to start."
I am displeased. We are getting nowhere at all. But again, I can do nothing. I must sit tight.

Owen phones me at work. He speaks strangely. "There are two words that are important, Mother," he tells me. "Remember these two words. *Medication* and *cooperation*." He repeats them. *"Medication* and *cooperation."* Now I know for sure. I know these speech patterns. Symbolistic words. Repetitive phrases. Owen is slipping once more. . . . He's slipping back. . . . *God help me.* . . . "What do you mean?" I ask, nonchalantly.

"When I get home, Mother, you must keep these two words in mind. *Medication* and *cooperation.*"

In the evening, he is restless. He craves cigars.
"Did you bring me more cigars?" There is no smile tonight.
"Yes. Here are some Cigarillos." I light one for him.
"I've got to get out of here," he states.
"You will. I'm sure it won't be much longer."
"I'm going to ask for a weekend pass."
"I don't know—I really think you should wait."
"For what, Mother? I've got to get out of here."
"Look," I try to reason, "give it a few more days. All right? In fact," I add, hesitantly, "I'm still thinking in terms of a transfer—to a private hospital. It will be much better for you. You'll get more attention."
He frowns. "I don't know—"
"Let's see how everything goes."
"I feel much better now."
"Look, tomorrow you're going to get a small dose of medication. I'd like you to stay on it awhile before you come home. Besides," I say cheerfully, "you said you're making something for me in physical therapy. What is it?"
"It's a copper plaque. It should be finished tomorrow."
"Good. I'd like to see it."
He puffs quietly for a while and then gets up and walks around. The restlessness is increasing.
"I think I'll watch some TV."

We enter the TV room but there are no available chairs.

"Looks like standing-room only," I quip.

Owen turns, and goes out into the corridor. Walking. Back and forth. Back and forth. I catch up to him.

"Would you like to play a game of Ping-Pong?" I suggest.

"Okay." He gets the paddles and ball from the nurse and we volley for a while. He quits after only a few minutes.

Visiting hours draw to a close. I kiss him good-night.

"What can I bring you tomorrow?" I ask.

"Cigars," he replies. "Bring plenty of cigars."

The next day I discover that the strain has taken its toll. I get to the hospital at the wrong time and can only spend twenty-five minutes with Owen.

"I've written a poem," he announces.

"Really?"

"Yes. It's for the hospital magazine. They ask the patients to contribute. Would you like to see it?"

"Of course."

He takes a sheet of paper out of his pocket and hands it to me. The printing, in pencil, is neat but shaky.

GETTING WELL AGAIN

It takes a pretty hour
to do it all again
to do it all
    all over
it takes a pretty hour to get it on
    again
but faith will win
    faith will triumph

"It's lovely, Owen. It's so full of hope. I'm sure they will print it."

"I'm going to rewrite it," he says, "in ink."

I have heard of Northview Hospital, a small, modern structure on the north shore of Long Island. It is a progressive place. A small, but pioneering place. It was the first hospital on Long

Island to allow fathers into the delivery room. That is good enough for me. I decide to call and ask for the psychiatric division.

"Yes," the head nurse tells me, "we do have a bed available in our psychiatric ward. When would you like to bring your son in?"

"Well," I answer, totally disarmed and delighted, "I can transfer him tomorrow. Will that be all right?"

"That will be fine. Try to get him here about noon."

"By the way, could you tell me who will be treating him there?"

"We can assign him to our chief psychiatrist, Dr. Glenn."

"That will be excellent," I tell her, totally relieved. "I will try to be there by midday."

I am elated. At long last, Owen will be in a private hospital under the care of a full-fledged psychiatrist, not a young, inexperienced resident. He will be taken care of properly and will get the individual attention he so desperately needs for his complete recovery.

I phone Vincent at his office.

"Sounds good to me," he says.

"Anything will be an improvement," I reply.

I am somewhat concerned about Owen's reaction to this change. However, I am determined to carry it through. He must be treated promptly and properly. It may already be too late. . . .

16

CLOSED PASSAGE

"I'm taking him out. This morning."

"Wait a minute," the nurse says. "The doctor will have to sign him out."

"I'm signing him out," I assert. "Right now." I walk briskly down to Owen's room. He is sitting on the bed. "Let's get your things together. We're leaving now."

"Where are we going?"

"Northview Hospital. They have a bed for you. And a good doctor. Come on."

He gathers all his belongings together and we place them in a large shopping bag. We walk down to the nurses' station.

"I want you to know," I inform the head nurse, "that I'm transferring my son to Northview Hospital. They will call for his records."

"I've called the doctor. She's on her way here now," the nurse says. "Please wait."

"I'm only waiting for a few minutes," I tell her. "I'll be in the reception room."

Owen and I go down the main corridor and wait in the large entry-room, near the elevator bank.

Dr. Arbo comes running out. "Why are you going?" she asks, a hurt expression on her face. "He's got to be checked out first."

"There's nothing to check out," I say. "We're going right

over to Northview Hospital. And we're going to get him well."

"Do you know what date this is, Mother?" Owen asks as we get into the car.

"No," I reply.

"It's December seventh."

He is, as always, a student of history.

As we drive north on the parkway, I notice an increasing irritability on his part. He is annoyed by my chatter, as I babble on, excessively. I only want to cheer him up. The transfer is difficult for him and I want to distract him, get his mind on other things.

He turns to me, angrily. "Mother, will you shut up!"

His face is a mask of tension. Is it this unwelcome change, or vestiges of illness? . . .

As we approach the hospital, I brave a comment. "Look how attractive it is. It's only three stories high, and very modern. You can really get to know everyone in a place like this." He only frowns more deeply, lips tightly clenched.

"Well," I say, as we walk toward the main entrance, "I did this to help you, Owen. We were getting nowhere fast at the medical center. I'm sure," I smile, "it will only be for a very short while."

Little did we know that it would be twenty-one more days of pain and suffering.

17

SANCTUARY

They are decorating a Christmas tree in the lobby. Colorful handmade trinkets are being placed on its plastic branches. Silver garlands swoop gracefully around the boughs. We watch as a silver star is placed at the top. It glitters. Welcoming us.

As we wait outside the admitting office, I continue to chatter, not realizing how confused Owen is becoming. By the time he is interviewed by the admitting clerk, the pieces of that glorious puzzle have once again begun to fall apart. She hands him a form and instructs him to fill out his reason for seeking admission to the hospital. This is an intellectual task he is ill-prepared for. He writes: *I am coming to the hospital for vague treatment.* And he puts down the doctor's initials.

We are now inside the North Ward, the psychiatric division. Mrs. Rudell, the head nurse introduces herself. "The doctor will be here shortly. In the meantime, here is a copy of the visitor's guidelines. Perhaps you can go over it together."

Dear Visitor:

The Administration and Staff of Northview Hospital's Psychiatric Unit wish to reassure you that the care, treatment, and rehabilitation of the patient is our main goal. The Unit strives to maintain the dignity of the patient with complete integrity on the part of the staff. For this attitude to be maintained, we ask the help of visitors and present guidelines for them.

I attempt to discuss the rules with Owen. But he is restless. He gets up, puffing on a cigar, and paces the long, narrow corridor.

"Let's look around," I suggest. We walk down the corridor, away from the small nurses' station, and find an all-purpose dayroom. A rectangular wooden table, rather large, is in the center of the room, surrounded by nonmatching chairs. Against the walls are several vinyl chairs and and one vinyl sofa. There are magazine racks, an old phonograph, records, and a TV set. I am later to find out that the patients do not take their meals here. They are served in their rooms.

Only a couple of patients are sitting here now. They are dressed in street clothes except for one young woman who wears a robe. She looks pale and sickly and is mumbling to herself. The patients seated here today are all young.

Mrs. Rudell comes in. "Oh, there you are," she chirps. "Dr. Glenn has just come in. If you step out to the nurses' station you can meet him."

"Very good," I comment. "By the way, I notice that you are not in uniform."

"No. We do not wear uniforms here. That makes it more comfortable for the patients."

"That's wonderful," I say. "My only problem is I may have trouble locating a nurse when I need one."

"No cause for concern," she replies. "You'll get to know us soon enough."

As we go out into the corridor I immediately spot the doctor, leaning against the countertop at the nurses' station. He is of medium height, lean, with chestnut brown hair, and appears to be in his late forties. As he turns toward us, I notice the kind face, the warm brown eyes.

"Nice to meet you." He greets us both with a hearty handshake. I like him immediately. There is something natural and sincere about this man. I can feel the vibes.

We go into his adjoining office and I finally pour everything out.

"He's been at the medical center twice," I say, "for a total of about five weeks, and each time they took him off medication before he was completely well. He's had nothing now for eight days."

"I'm really shocked," he say, "that he's not on any major tranquilizer at the moment."

"He had a terrible reaction to Haldol," I continue, recounting in detail the progress, or rather the retrogression, of his illness, describing the parkinsonian symptoms, the fall, the stay at home, and finally, the relapse.

"He definitely must be on medication. And at once," Dr. Glenn declares. "You needn't be concerned about adverse reactions to Haldol and Thorazine, as there are many, many other antipsychotic drugs available now for treatment."

He turns now to Owen. "Well, young man, I'll like to hear what has caused your problem in the first place."

Owen smiles slyly. "I guess it was marijuana," he admits. "I smoked a lot of it. Every night. Everyone did at college. Anyway, I smoked pot every night and then I got some stuff which had angel dust in it. That's what made me blow my mind."

"I see," the doctor says, deep concern on his face. "I'll tell you something. Angel dust is pretty dangerous stuff. There's nothing worse on the drug scene today. But marijuana is pretty dangerous, too. And if you smoke enough of it, it can do some very deadly things to your mind."

"I guess you're right," Owen concedes.

"The brain is a very delicate, complicated, and sensitive organ," the doctor states, "and when you start fooling around with drugs, especially on a regular basis, you are in for trouble." He turns to me. "My own feeling is that *all* mental illness, whether drug-induced or not, is caused by chemical changes in the brain."

"That's a very interesting theory," I reply. "From the research I've been doing, more and more psychiatrists are coming to the same conclusion."

"Well, of course, there is still a good deal of controversy on the subject."

"Yes, I am aware of that."

"Now," he says, "since you are a concerned parent, and a fairly knowledgeable one, I will be quite open with you regarding Owen's treatment here. We will be starting him on medication today, and since you are worried about possible side effects with both Haldol and Thorazine—and believe me, both drugs are potent enough to produce them—I will be giving him a different drug. It's called Taractan."

"Thank you for keeping me informed. Now, if I have to reach you for any reason, is there any special time that I can call?"

"Mrs. Etons, I work a full week, and that includes Saturday and Sunday. You can speak to me here, seven days a week, between the hours of twelve noon and two. In addition, I have a private practice nearby. You can always leave a message at my office."

I am relieved. At long last, Owen and I have found the right doctor. I only hope the course of treatment is the right one. And that we haven't lost too much precious time.

In the evening, when I visit the hospital, Owen is extremely listless. He lies on his bed, unable to move, unwilling to talk. I walk down to the nurses' station and speak to the night nurse.

"It's the medication," she tells me. "They all react the same way in the beginning. It will take a day or two for him to adjust to it."

Hardly comforted, I return to Owen's room. He has taken the phone off the hook. I put the receiver back in place.

"How are you feeling?" I ask.

"Very sleepy," he responds.

"I'm going to leave soon. You should get a good night's sleep. It's been a busy day." I glance about the large, square room. It is a semi-private accommodation, containing four beds. There are four large windows, looking out on a parking lot. The room is on the first floor.

Three other young men share this room with Owen. They are all pleasant, but extremely quiet, evidently from medication. And they all smoke heavily.

I turn back to Owen. He has again taken the phone off the hook. This concerns me. "I'm not going to be able to call you if you keep doing this," I say. "Please leave the phone alone."

"I'm very tired," he says. "I'm going to sleep now."

"Get a good night's rest, dear. I'll see you tomorrow." I cover him, kiss him on the cheek, and tiptoe out of the room.

I have done the right thing, I tell myself in the car. We have found a sanctuary here. And we have found Dr. Glenn.

18

OF DRUGS AND DEMONS

Our sanctuary has failed us. Perhaps we have not made it in time. The medicine does not work. Owen gets worse. The doctor tries a different medication or combination of medications every day. He appears to be playing with Owen's body chemistry. And Owen is so slightly built, I am concerned. The chemical barrage continues: Taractan, Serentil, Tranxene, Haldol, Cogentin, and God knows what else, and in what combination. And Owen gets worse. And worse. And worse. . . .

On the morning of December eighth, I call the hospital. I am in a positive, happy mood. Mrs. Rudell shatters it. In one swift sentence.

"Your son was quite agitated this morning."

In the evening, I visit Owen. He appears to be rational. The agitation of the morning is clearly not in evidence.

We are in his room. He is lying, listlessly, in bed.

"It's the medication that is making you so tired," I tell him. "They've changed to something else today. The drug they gave you yesterday had a bad effect on you this morning."

"I know."

"Look, you're going to be fine soon. Just take your medicine and get plenty of rest. Pretend you're on vacation. That's all you have to do."

"Yeah. *Some* vacation."

"I've brought you several magazines. Would you like to see them now?"

"No. My eyes can't focus."

I place the magazines on his night table. I notice the phone is on the hook.

We spend a quiet hour together. Owen introduces me to two of his roommates: Blake, a handsome seventeen-year-old, and Ron, a young man in his mid-twenties. Both are friendly, but appear to be very depressed. The fourth roommate has just been discharged.

Owen is too drowsy to communicate. I chatter in my usual way, occasionally making a comment to Blake and Ron. They, too, do not seem to wish to talk.

Mental illness can be as painful as physical illness. When you hurt, you do not wish to talk.

Owen keeps dozing off. "I'm very tired," he repeats.

"I'm going to go now. You go to sleep." I kiss him good-night and leave.

Perhaps, I say to myself in the car, this quiescence is a positive sign. Perhaps the restlessness and irritability which were so noticeable when we arrived yesterday are now under control. He certainly is not agitated now. Perhaps Serentil, the drug he is now taking, is the answer.

But Owen gets worse. I find this out during my routine morning call to the hospital the next day. And Mrs. Rudell sounds very unhappy with the situation.

"He was very disruptive this morning," she states. "Really difficult to control."

"What was he doing?" I ask.

"Cursing quite a bit, for one thing."

"I see. Well, I will be there this afternoon."

I telephone Owen. "Hi, how are you today?" I ask, casually.

"All right. I'm getting ready to leave."

"To leave?"

"Yes. Didn't you know? I'm coming home today."

"Well—I don't think that's such a good idea."

"Why not?"

"It's very cold out today. And it's raining. Let's wait until the weather gets better."

"But, Mother, I want to leave today!"

"Look, I'll be there at two. We can talk about it then."

The doors to the North Ward are locked. One must ring a bell for admission. There is a mirror and a buzzer at the nurses' station. Mrs. Rudell buzzes me in.

As I enter, I see Owen walking down the corridor toward me. He is wearing two flowers in his buttonhole. And he is smiling.

"Hello, Owen."

"Hello, Mother. Did you come on the SST?"

Did you come on the SST?

"No, dear," I reply, "I came by car." I take his arm in mine. His hands are shaking slightly. We walk down to the dayroom together. And I sit, quietly, with my sick son. What can I do? What can I say?

Dr. Glenn greets me in the corridor as I am about to leave. "He was very disruptive this morning," he says, "so we had to give him an injection of Haldol. A very small dose," he adds, for my benefit, "and some Valium to quiet him."

"He's worse," I say.

"I know."

"He's worse than he was when I brought him here two days ago."

"Mrs. Etons, he's worse because he was on no medication at all. Your son was going downhill when you brought him here because of that fact. And that fact alone. We're trying to find the right medication for him. We're trying to help him."

"He's being treated like a pincushion. All he gets are different injections every day."

"Let's see what progress he makes. It takes a little while."

"It's taken a long while. He's been ill a very long while." I turn, and walk out the door.

It is now Saturday, and I am at work. I try, fruitlessly, to phone Owen. I cannot get through to him on his phone. When I call the nurses' station, I am told that he is asleep. They inform me that they have moved him to a room close to the nurses' station. A room without a telephone.

Vincent calls me in the afternoon. He has just been to the hospital. Owen is much worse.

"Say no more," I tell him. "I will come home early."

At home, I phone an old friend of my parents. She is a psychiatrist with a practice in New York City. We talk at length about Owen, and she is able to give me the name of a psychiatrist, who, coincidentally, is in charge of the Day Hospital at the Long Island Medical Center. He is an old friend and colleague of hers by the name of Hilliard French. He will help me, she says,

"Yes," Dr. French states, "I know Dr. Glenn."

"Can you tell me something about him?" I ask.

"He and I do not have the same approach to the treatment of mental illness," he replies. "Dr. Glenn believes that all mental illness is organic in origin and he relies heavily on drugs."

I speak to Vincent on the way to the hospital. "At least Dr. Glenn is well known here on the Island. And he believes that mental illness is caused by chemical changes in the brain, not by someone looking at you the wrong way when you were in your formative years. And *that* is good enough for me. In fact," I add, "I'm beginning to feel positive about him again."

"I have no complaints with him," Vince says.

When we arrive at Northview, we find Owen on his bed. He is very groggy.

"Let's get him up and give him some coffee," Vince suggests.

"Good idea," I reply.

There is a small kitchen next to the nurses' station. Inside, there is always fresh coffee as well as hot water for tea and hot chocolate, packets of which are on the counter. I bring Owen a cup of the coffee. I have been generous with the sugar.

"Here, drink this," I urge. He takes a sip, then sits back, drowsily, on his chair.

"Let's walk around," Vince says, getting him up on his feet.
We treat him like a drunk, walking him back and forth in
the long corridor. For, indeed, he is drunk. He is intoxicated
with drugs. Remnants of angel dust, comingling with major
tranquilizers.

"Rabbi, I know you don't know me, but we are members of
your congregation." I am sobbing. "I want you to do something
for me. You see, it's my son. He came home from college—
and he's been very ill—very ill—and they keep giving him drugs,
different kinds of drugs every day—and he's getting worse and
worse . . ." My voice breaks off.
    "What would you like me to do for you?"
    "Please—will you say a prayer for him tonight? I'm not a
religious person. I've never really believed in organized religion
—but my son is sick—he's so very sick—"
    "I understand."
    "Please, then, just say a little prayer."

They lock him up. He is put into a small isolation room opposite the nurses' station. That is the only way they can control
him. For over the weekend, Owen has become quite violent.
Verbally and physically violent.
    I find him sitting, tied to a chair. They have imprisoned him
in the corridor, opposite the nurses' station. This is their method
of "controlling his behavior." "Untie him at once," I instruct the
orderly. He undoes the ropes across Owen's shoulders and arms.
    I take him into the dayroom. He is now in a state of sheer
panic. His eyes gleam wildly and his body trembles.
    What forces have unleashed this nameless fear? This total,
debilitating terror?
    Strange, psychic demons have taken hold of him. Demons,
conjured up by drugs, are now eating away at his brain, devour-
ing his normal thought processes, until all that is left is an
absolute, all-consuming terror. They have taken possession of
him once more. These Demons of Madness. . . .
    Owen is shaking more strongly. I put my arms around him.

"Would you like to get dressed, Owen? Come on; it's chilly in here." We go into his room. He takes the clothes off the chair and proceeds to put his shirt and pants on first, his underwear on top. "No," I tell him, "you've got it all backward."

Dr. Glenn meets me in the hall. "Tomorrow I want to have a conference with you and your husband. We're going to sit down together and work out a new course of action."

Owen and I go into the kitchen for some refreshments. He mixes tea with hot chocolate and proceeds to drink it down. I don't even try to stop him.

There is nothing I can do. I must sit, helplessly. He is no longer part of my world.

Strings of significant Sundays. Tied together by connecting beads, phases of illness. It is Sunday once more. Our day to hold an important conference with the psychiatrist. And like others before it, this is again a significant Sunday.

Owen is groggy. Yet he is hyperactive. Strange dichotomy of behavior, brought about by the combination of mental illness and wondrously potent chemicals. Chemicals treating the effects of chemicals. Drugs. Demons. He cannot be restrained, but stalks the long corridor, controlled by these strong forces, mumbling incoherently. His sister strives to keep up with his rapid pace.

"I am going to be quite open with you," Dr. Glenn tells us, later, in his office. "I have brought Owen's chart with me to try to show you what we have been doing. Yes, we have been trying different drugs on him. As a matter of fact," he adds, "I have him back on Serentil at the moment and, as you can see, it is doing nothing for him at all."

"It's so hard for me to understand," I say, "for the whole family to understand. We are all so discouraged now. Three times he has been in the throes of a deep psychosis. Three times he has been tortured like this—"

"I know," the doctor states, "but we are going to take new action today. Drastic action, perhaps, but it will work. It *has* worked, with other patients who were as sick as your son."

"What do you suggest?" Vince wants to know.

"We have to administer a super-bombardment of Haldol, a round-the-clock series of injections."

"Oh, no! You—"

He waves me quiet with his hand. "I know what you're going to say. That he's allergic to Haldol. That he's had a bad reaction to Haldol, and so on. But that's sheer nonsense. The only reason he had such terrible side effects with the Haldol in the first place is that the doctors at the medical center are too conservative. They want to take what they think is the safest approach. But it isn't always. If Owen had had Cogentin from the very beginning, along with the Haldol, he would never have developed the parkinsonian symptoms in the first place. Do you understand what I'm saying?"

"Yes," I reply.

"So you're suggesting Haldol again?" Vince asks.

"Yes. And I'm only sorry that I didn't start it as soon as your son was admitted here last Wednesday. If I had, he might be all right now."

"What do you mean by super-bombardment?" I ask. "How much will you be giving him?" I am apprehensive.

"It is a pretty strenuous regimen of injections for the first day, but then we gradually reduce the dosage. Let me explain it to you in detail. On the first day, that will be tomorrow, we give him six shots, one hour apart, each injection consisting of five milligrams of Haldol; then we give him one five-milligram shot every six hours, along with the Cogentin. After a couple of days, we reduce the dosage from thirty milligrams daily to twenty milligrams daily, then down to ten, and so on."

"Whew!" Vince says. "Then what, if this doesn't work?"

"Then we will have to administer electroshock therapy."

"No!" I protest. "No electroshock." I could not subject my child to such barbaric physical abuse.

"What else do you suggest?" the doctor asks, openly annoyed. "If we can't control him here, then you might as well transfer him to a state hospital."

No. That, too, is no solution. I can protest no more.

"Look, Dr. Glenn, my wife and I have the utmost confidence

in you," says Vince, the diplomat. "If you know that this treatment has worked, and if you feel that it will make our son well again, then you have our permission to try it."

The doctor smiled once more. "Yes. I feel very strongly that this is the best course of action to take."

When we visit Owen again, in the evening, we notice that Dr. Glenn is still in the hospital. It is Sunday night; he has been there since noon, and he is still working. I come to the conclusion that he is very dedicated.

Yet, that night I cannot sleep. Every time I close my eyes, I picture Owen passively receiving these strong chemicals. Hour after hour they are pumped into his thin arms. They circulate ruthlessly through his slender body wreaking unknown, unseen, havoc. How can I permit this to happen? How can I allow my son to become a guinea pig?

No. It is too drastic a procedure. And I resolve to stop it.

Twice the next morning I phone the hospital and ask them to hold off. But when I arrive there at noon, they have already begun the bombardment. Every hour on the hour. As I sit in the dayroom with Owen, the young nurse, Marie, comes in and takes him away for his second shot. He goes, willingly.

It is quite amazing, the terms the medical profession itself uses for these treatments: *bombardment. Shots.* Terms of war. But, in a sense, we are waging a war here. A war against the demons.

"We had to start the procedure," Dr. Glenn tells me later, out in the corridor. "We had to control his behavior." The doctor seems to be as upset as the nurses now, for Owen had lost bladder control in the morning.

Yes. They have to control him. But it is not his behavior they are after. It is the strange psychic forces. The demons. Unleashed by the angel dust.

We walk down the corridor, Owen and I. At the very end of the hall glitters the lovely, decorated Christmas tree. When we get to the tree, Owen proceeds to remove the trinkets, putting them in his pockets.

He walks, aimlessly, up and down the long corridor, mumbling, smiling, eyes glazed. I am forced to walk with him. For Owen cannot sit still.

There is, however, a glimmer of rationality breaking through. He remembers telephone numbers. Bits of the puzzle appear to be in their proper place. Has the Haldol put them back?

My only concern, for he is calmer now, is the fact that his hands are still shaking. When I get ready to leave, at two, I speak to the nurse. She assures me—sweet Marie, I like her manner—that he is receiving Cogentin and that there is nothing to worry about.

Vincent and I visit in the evening. We have brought him the newspapers, and to our utter amazement, he sits and reads them. Vince sees a definite improvement.

"Owen," I explain, "I want you to know that you are getting these shots to make you better. They work much faster than pills." He seems to understand.

At eight o'clock, I walk him to his private room, and put him to bed for the night.

Owen has now been in the hospital for a total of forty-two days. And his brain is still sick. The illness has cast a pall over our normal family routine. I am never home for dinner anymore, since I go directly from work to the hospital. It is especially hard on Suzy, who must prepare the meals and care for her younger brother. Therefore, we have arranged for the children to fly down to Florida for the Christmas vacation. They will stay with their grandparents.

It is now December thirteenth. Owen has been on the super-Haldol routine for two days, and the improvement continues. Dr. Glenn examines him, in his office, in front of me.

"All right, Owen. Please do what I tell you. Hold your hands out like this," he demonstrates, "and spread your fingers apart."

The first time Owen tries, he fails. His hands are shaking. "Try again," the doctor encourages. Owen holds both hands out, shakily. Slowly, he spreads his fingers apart, one by one. He has succeeded. With one hand only. Owen smiles. And so do I.

Dr. Glenn takes me aside. "We're reducing the dosage of Haldol to a total of twenty milligrams a day, spreading out the shots. And, of course, he will continue to get the Cogentin. Now," he adds, "I really feel that in order to obtain more immediate results, we'd be best off giving him an electroshock treatment."

"Oh, no, doctor. You must give the Haldol a chance to work. It takes about a week. Please. Let's give it a little time."

Dr. Glenn seems somewhat impatient. It's as if he wants an instantaneous cure. I know Owen. And these episodes last about one week, once antipsychotic medication is begun. I now have developed the virtue of patience. With a drug-induced psychosis, one has no choice.

Owen is, once again, very close to the edge of health. When we arrive for our evening visit, there he is! Playing Ping-Pong with Ron. It is a happy sight, indeed.

However, the restlessness lingers. Suzy is with us, and she finds herself out in the corridor, again walking back and forth with her brother for the better part of the visit. Suzy, too, has learned patience.

But the socialization is short-lived. On the next afternoon, I find Owen sitting alone in his room, morose and silent. He is not quite out of the fog. "Come on," I encourage, "let's go out to the dayroom and see what's doing." His behavior, as we walk down the corridor, is somewhat bizarre. He has taken a sudden fascination to the floor tiles. "I have to be careful," he tells me. "I can't walk on the white ones." The chants of the Real World haunt me now. *Step on the crack. Break your mother's back. . . .*

There is a physical therapist in the dayroom today. She is standing at the head of the long wooden table, assisting several young patients who are in the process of making Christmas decorations for the walls.

"Would you like to help us?" she asks Owen. No. He is not yet ready to participate. We sit on the vinyl sofa and watch.

As I am leaving, Dr. Glenn comes over to me and grabs my hand, smiling warmly. "I'm very pleased with Owen's progress."

"Yes, he is slowly improving," I respond.

"We should have done this sooner," he adds.

I must admit, he is right.

In the evening, Vince and I visit, bringing Owen the daily newspapers. He sits and reads them for fifteen minutes. This is certainly an excellent sign of approaching recovery. However, while reading an article about a fatal plane crash, he laughs. His behavior is still not quite appropriate.

Inertia. That is the word that best describes the results of the Haldol circulating through the bloodstream. The body becomes so slowed down, it cannot even move. Owen demonstrates this phenomenon when I make my visit to Northview on Thursday. He is lying, motionless, on his bed. Undressed. It is noon.

"Come, I've brought you a chocolate malted from the coffee shop. Get your clothes on and let's go out to the dayroom for a little change of scenery."

He gets dressed, but he is exceptionally quiet and serious. And he seems tense. However, I am determined to help him overcome it. We walk down to the dayroom and sit at the table while he drinks his malted. He is still uncommunicative. It is rather discouraging. But his mood is now beyond his own control.

As we are leafing through one of the news magazines, we notice an article about World War Two and the African campaign. I make some comments about the war and General Rommel, and Owen replies by mentioning the animals in Africa. Now, I think I understand what Dr. Sand meant when he mentioned "looseness of thought."

Before I leave, I look for Dr. Glenn. I find him in the nurses' station.

"It's the fourth day on Haldol," I say, "and he's improving, but slowly."

"Yes. In fact, we are so pleased with his progress that we are discontinuing the injections. He will be getting Haldol by mouth now."

Progress. We are reaching the edge of health. But we still have a little way to go, and the uncharted road is a bit bumpy.

It is Friday afternoon and Owen looks exceptionally good. His skin is fresh and clear, his eyes are alert, and the easy charm is in evidence.

"You look terrific!" I say.

We go into the dayroom and chat for a while.

"I'd like to come home," he says.

"Well, I'm very happy to hear you say that. However, we will have to wait a little while longer."

"How much longer?"

"I don't know. I'll have to speak to the doctor."

"I hope it's soon."

"Look, Owen, I want you to know something. You are not going to go back to college this coming semester. We want you to rest a little bit longer." He seems relieved.

I hand him the newspapers and he turns the pages slowly. After a few minutes of reading the international news, he turns to me. "We have to watch out for the Russians," he cautions. "They are getting very powerful. Very powerful."

We take a stroll down the hall and Owen goes back into his former semi-private room. It is empty. He walks over to Blake's night table, picks up his tiny portable radio, and stuffs it into his pocket. "Owen," I protest, "that is not yours. Please put it back." He only smiles.

As I leave, I ask for Dr. Glenn. This mixture of rationality with irrationality concerns me. Mrs. Rudell says that the doctor has just left for the day.

In the evening, in four short hours, Owen seems greatly improved. We find him in his room, in bed. He looks more tired now, but he is consistently more rational.

It is now Saturday, and I decide to phone the hospital and ask them to change Owen back to his old room.

"I'm sure you'll be happy to know," Marie says, "that he was just switched back this morning. You can phone him directly again."

Now I know for sure that he has made it over the edge. I call him immediately. Our talk on the phone is very encouraging. He is able to sustain a rational conversation.

I enter the hospital lobby a few minutes early and sneak a look through the glass panes in the double doors leading to the North Ward. A pleasant sight greets me. Owen is playing Ping-Pong with Blake.

Our visit, however, seems strained tonight. Remnants of strange speech return. "Guilt, Mother, guilt," he says. And later, he mentions the Russians. "The Russians have power, tremendous power," he states.

I try to clear his mind, to ignore this setback, and to cheer him. "Owen, your high school is holding its annual Christmas concert this coming Thursday night. You received an invitation in the mail. Would you like to go?"

"Yes. Very much."

"Well, I'll speak to Dr. Glenn and see if he'll let you have a weekend pass."

He seems pleased with the prospect.

Dr. Glenn vetoes the pass. For technical reasons, having to do with our health insurance, Owen will not be allowed out of the hospital.

I tell Owen it is just as well that he cannot attend, because he will be coming home soon, anyway. "Besides," I add, "I have an excellent idea."

"What?"

"I will go and see Miss James, the choir director, and ask if we can have a tape of the concert. Would you like that?"

"Sure." But I know he is very disappointed. And I realize that I made a tactical error in suggesting the concert before I checked it out with the doctor.

"He's doing much better," Dr. Glenn tells me on Monday.

"How much medication is he getting now?"

"We're keeping him on the same level at present. Twenty milligrams. It will be just for a little while longer."

"Fine. I really don't want you to reduce it yet."

"Why?"

"Because he's still talking about the Russians."

The doctor smiles. "Look, he may very well talk about the Russians after he gets home. I wouldn't be concerned about that."

But I am concerned. For Owen has the Russians, Soviet Power, the Bomb, and the Middle East on his mind. Constantly. For him, we are on the brink of war.

19

THE RUSSIANS ARE GOING;
THE RUSSIANS ARE GOING

On Thursday, December twenty-first, Suzy and Tim leave New York in a cold, blustery rainstorm and fly down to the warmth, sunshine, and tranquility of southeastern Florida.

Dr. Glenn tells us that Owen should be out of the hospital in one week.

Medication has now been reduced to ten milligrams of Haldol per day.

Owen is informed that he now has the privilege of going out to the hospital coffee shop.

The demons die, and the Russians retreat to a safe distance.

Owen is once more on the edge of health. And this time, he has an experienced, dedicated doctor and a caring family who work together to pull him up and over that edge so that his grasp is secure. Now there will be no slipping back.

"They're both getting shock treatments," Owen explains.

"Both?" I ask.

"Yes. They're very depressed."

"I noticed that from the beginning."

We are talking about Blake and Ron, both of whom are still so quiet, so morose.

"Is Dr. Glenn treating them?"

"No. It's the other doctor you see in here quite a bit. I think his name is Carpetti. I'm not sure."

"Well," I tell him, "I'm sure they'll soon be better. Anyway, let's talk about you. You're doing so well that Dr. Glenn is reducing your dosage of Haldol to eight milligrams a day. And after you're home for a while, he will reduce it still further."

"When am I getting out of here?"

"On December twenty-eighth. And that is definite."

"Good. I can't wait to play my guitar."

"And I can't wait to hear you."

"I'm not that good, yet."

"But if you practice, you will be."

"I guess you're right." He leans back on the pillow. He is extremely tired today. He has slept almost the entire day, and although he has gotten dressed for my benefit, he is still in his room. The Haldol is having a powerful effect on his body.

On Thursday, December twenty-second, a milestone is reached at Northview. Owen is allowed out to the coffee shop with me.

As we sit at our tiny table and talk, I notice that his speech is a bit stiff and halting. A result, no doubt, of the potent medication.

Still each day there is gradual, steady improvement in Owen's condition. His mood is excellent, his behavior appropriate. Fatigue is a daily problem, for medication slows him down. Yet restlessness lingers. He cannot sit very long, and his wanderings through the ward are happy ones. His speech is rational. His fears realistic. He ceases to warn us of the Russians. War is no longer imminent.

"Here, Owen, I've gotten you a tape of the Christmas concert. I saw Miss James this morning and she said it's yours to keep. They've done the *Messiah*, as always."

He takes the tape. "Thanks very much."

"Next year in Jerusalem."

He looks at me, quizzically.

"It's a beautiful old expression. From a prayer, I believe. 'Next year in Jerusalem'—you'll be with them then. And you'll be singing the *Messiah,* too."

Owen's spirits continue to soar with each passing day. He has something beautiful to look forward to. Home.

I'm going to get a stereo," he tells me.

"That's a very good idea."

"And I'll concentrate on my guitar. Suzy knows a teacher I can go to when I'm ready."

"Terrific."

"Only—I wish we had the piano."

"Yes, I know. But we'll have it back again. As soon as we've found a house here on the Island, the piano and all of our furniture will be shipped back. And then, perhaps, we'll rent the house in Florida. Or sell it." I think, briefly, of Tim and Suzy sunning themselves at this very moment, and I glance out the window at the cold, gray sky. If only Owen and I could be with them now, basking in that beneficial warmth . . . if only. . . .

"Dr. Sand!"

"Mrs. Etons!"

"What a pleasant surprise."

"Imagine meeting here."

We are in a well-known bookstore.

"How is Owen?"

"Doing very well, thanks. How are you?"

"Just fine. I'm getting married tomorrow."

"How wonderful. I'll bet she's a nurse."

"You've won."

"I want to wish you the very best."

"Thanks so much."

"You know, it's coincidental, but Owen is being discharged from Northview tomorrow."

"Is he? That's marvelous."

"Yes. And now I won't forget your wedding date."

"No. I can see why not."

"Good luck."

"The same to you."

The last two days at the hospital are pleasant, uneventful ones. Owen rests, reads a little, and makes plans to come home.

I make plans, too, with Vincent. We must get out of the cramped apartment. But we cannot make a move until Suzy graduates from high school in June. And we must find a house close to whichever college Owen chooses. Yet, we can't discuss college with him now. We must wait a little while longer. So, for the present, Vince and I are in limbo, too.

On the morning of Wednesday, December twenty-eighth, Dr. Glenn prepares to discharge his most difficult patient from Northview. Owen has now spent a total of eight weeks, fifty-six days, in the hospital.

We follow the doctor into his office. "Now, I am giving you two prescriptions," he tells Owen. "One for Haldol and one for Cogentin. I've written out the schedule for you on this card." He hands him a three by five index card. "Now, you must follow this schedule precisely."

He hands me the prescriptions. "How long will he be staying at this dosage level?" I want to know.

"That will depend on how he does. I will be seeing him in my office next Friday. Now, Owen, after Friday, I can see you every two weeks, and later, we can spread out the visits to every three weeks, then once a month, until we taper off. But, while you're on medication, and you will be on for some time, it's important for me to see you."

"Okay, doctor," Owen replies.

"Yes, doctor, I definitely want Owen to see you on a regular basis," I add.

"And, of course, we must find a good program for you, at one of the local hospitals. We don't have outpatient facilities, but I will have our social worker make arrangements and contact you."

"I really appreciate that," I tell him.

"Thanks for everything, doctor," Owen says, smiling warmly. They shake hands.

It is a cold, crisp winter's day. We stop, momentarily, outside the front door of the hospital and deeply breathe in the sharp, fresh air. As we walk down the steps, Owen turns to me.

"You know, I've spent three holidays in the hospital."

"Really? Which ones?"

"Halloween, Thanksgiving, and Christmas."

"I hadn't thought of it before."

But Owen had. For he is a student of history. And dates are of the utmost importance to a student of history.

20

HOME FREE

Owen is home once more, and our life is back to nearly normal. There are still precautions to take: medication at certain times of the day, visits to the psychiatrist, arrangements for his outpatient care.

The first few days are restful ones. No one thinks in terms of the future. We take one day at a time.

Owen is still somewhat tired. He sleeps a good deal of the time; the medication level is still quite high.

His mood continues to be pleasant. However, I notice certain physical problems. He walks rather stiffly, and his speech is slurred. These must be, I reason, continued side effects from the Haldol. It is distressing, but for now it must be. We can never slip back. . . .

On Thursday, the day after his release from the hospital, Owen's college friend Randy comes over for a visit. He is now home for Christmas vacation.

"Hey, Owen!" he bellows, "you look great! Just great!"

"Thanks." Owen beams.

The two young men spend a congenial afternoon together. I keep discreetly away while they reminisce. I am pleased that Owen has a visitor. Especially so soon. It is very good for his morale. And, to my great relief, he smokes only one cigar the entire afternoon.

On Saturday, Vincent must go to Kennedy Airport to pick up Suzy and Tim. So I take Owen to work with me.

The day progresses smoothly. Owen is able to rest and read while he waits for me.

After work, we stop to do some shopping at a local department store. By the time we arrive home, Owen is thoroughly exhausted. The long day has been too hectic for him. He is, after all, still recuperating.

Sunday, however, is a happy, restful day. Just the way it used to be. A typical suburban Sunday. Nothing special to do. Tables piled high with the Sunday *Times* and *Newsday*. Television set blaring the football game. No schedule to keep, except the medication. On this, there can be no flexibility.

We are all so happy now on this significantly peaceful Sunday.

Owen strums lightly on his guitar, singing softly.

Timmy plays with his electric trains.

Suzy is intently blow-drying her long, auburn tresses.

Vince notices interference on his football game and wants to know who's using the hair dryer.

And I—I am marveling at the wondrousness of having the family together again like this. To be able to have a quiet Sunday once more. And not to have to go to the hospital.

During the following week, as promised by Dr. Glenn, the social worker at Northview calls.

"I have made a placement for Owen," she tells me, "at the Day Hospital at the Long Island Medical Center. The director would like you to phone. Her name is Mrs. Morris."

I thank the social worker, and immediately speak to Owen. He is in his room, softly playing his guitar.

"There's an opening for you at the Day Hospital at the medical center. I'm calling now. I wanted you to know about it first." He doesn't look too happy. "What's the matter?"

"Why can't I just stay home?"

"There's not enough for you to do at home."

"Sure there is. I have my guitar, books, music—"

"No," I say firmly. Can I tell him of my fears? My apprehensions? "It isn't good for you to be alone," I explain. "Especially when you're on medication. You might get drowsy. Who knows? Anyway, you're much better off at the Day Hospital."

"I don't know—"

"Well, Dr. Glenn does. And he says it's the best thing to do right now."

Owen still isn't convinced. He doesn't seem to realize just how very sick he has been.

"Okay," he reluctantly agrees. "I guess I'll go."

I phone Mrs. Morris. "Yes," she says, "we can accept your son."

"Well," I tell Owen, "you'll be going to the Day Hospital for only three hours a day for the first month. After that, you'll be on the full-day program. That should be nice."

"Yeah," he agrees, "until something better comes along." He goes back to his song.

21

THE HEALING

The human body is truly a wondrous machine. It can take a tremendous amount of punishment, both mental and physical. Yet, when it is seriously impaired, either by accident or illness, it needs a very long time to heal. The more severe the illness, the longer the healing process.

Owen has been very, very ill. The dosage of angel dust was a moderate one; had it been smaller, he would have been well in very short order. He would have been woozy; perhaps he would have hallucinated briefly. But he would not have "freaked out."

"It will take anywhere from three months to one year for him to be perfectly well again," Dr. Glenn informs us. "With the combination of time and medication, the biogenic amine levels in his brain, particularly dopamine, will be back to where they should be."

We are in the doctor's office for our first regular visit. It has been nine days since Owen's discharge from the hospital. He was fine in the car on the way over, but now he is not quite coherent. He has just mumbled something to the doctor.

Dr. Glenn turns to me, a pained expression on his face. "This is not normal," he says.

"I realize that," I respond. And yet, at home, Owen has appeared to be quite rational. He has functioned well in the daily routine. Could it be the excitement of coming to the doctor's office that has triggered this slight relapse?

"As you see," the doctor is saying, "it all takes time."

"Yes, I am learning the art of patience," I tell him. The doctor's explanation is, most likely, the correct one. The chemicals in Owen's brain are still not quite in proper balance. We must wait. It is only January.

"I am reducing his medication from eight milligrams to six milligrams of Haldol per day." Dr. Glenn hands me the new schedule card.

"Will it be all right to reduce it now when he's—like this?" I ask.

"Yes. Perfectly all right. As I just explained to you, it will take up to a full year for him to be completely back to normal."

One year. That is a long time. Even in a young life.

Owen is now enrolled in the Day Hospital at the Long Island Medical Center. It is located in an old, three-story building behind the new hospital, and next to the structure that houses the outpatient clinic. The building itself is the mental health center of the hospital complex. Yet, strangely enough, the Day Hospital is housed in the basement. A rather dreary location, I feel. Yet, I cannot voice my feelings to Owen. He needs the activities, the care, the support it provides at this time. Above all else, his healing must be assured.

All of the patients' activities take place in the rather drab basement. Except for two: lunch, which is held in the new hospital's cafeteria, and physical therapy, which takes place in the gym, located in yet another old building. There is a connecting network of subterranean tunnels through which the patients travel from one building to another.

On the first day, I walk Owen in to help him find the group. As we walk down the old staircase, we see a fairly large group of people coming toward us, led by a rather authoritarian-looking woman. She looks rather severely at me.

"Yes, may I help you?" she demands.

"We are looking for the Day Hospital."

"Are you Mrs. Etons?"

"Yes," I reply, "and this is my son Owen."

"I'm Mrs. Morris," she states. "It really wasn't necessary for you to walk him down."

"I'm sorry," I apologize, "but I was just trying to help him find the right place." Can I tell her how very sick he has been? No. She is annoyed. I have violated her turf. But I have a son who is still sick, who still needs my help.

Owen's adjustment in the Day Hospital is an easy one, especially during January, when he only attends on a part-time basis.

My life is more complicated, however, since I must take him each day and then pick him up and bring him back to work with me. On certain days, if the other children are home, I can take him directly home. He still cannot be left alone under any circumstances.

His thought processes are occasionally bizarre. On one inclement winter's day, after it had been alternately raining and snowing for hours, Owen and I are driving home. There have been hazardous driving warnings on the radio for the entire day. Yet, as we drive along in this downpour, Owen asks a rather strange question.

"Do you think that, perhaps, they have been scientifically seeding the clouds to make the rain?"

"Owen," I decide to be straightforward, "you are not being rational."

He laughs, good-naturedly.

"There's a definite improvement," Dr. Glenn states, emphatically. "I am very, very pleased."

It is near the end of January now, and we are in the doctor's office.

"What about his medication?" I ask.

"I am reducing it again. He will now get four milligrams of Haldol per day, and one milligram Cogentin." He hands Owen the new schedule card. "How do you feel about that?" he asks him.

"Very good," Owen replies. Tonight, he is in an extremely relaxed mood.

One afternoon, at the very end of January, Owen surprises me by asking for something interesting to read. He would like a book. It is the first time that he has shown interest in reading a complete book. His attention span has heretofore been limited to newspapers and magazines. But today he would like a book. I give him *The Kitchen Sink Papers*. It is delightful, light reading. Perfect for one who has had trouble concentrating. But now, with his medication again reduced, Owen is able to concentrate for longer and longer periods. It is quite wonderful.

February begins, and Owen now attends the Day Hospital on a full-time basis. There is a complete program for him now, including lunch, every day. He explains it to me in detail.

"We have Physical Therapy, Occupational Therapy, and Group Therapy."

"What do you do in Physical Therapy?" I ask.

"Well, we go to the gym and we have different activities each time. Sometimes we dance, or we just move to the music. Other times we throw sponge balls around. And, of course, we play games. Volleyball, basketball, and European handball, mostly."

"That sounds pretty exciting."

"I like the acting the best."

"You act?"

"Yes. We sit around and read scripts of different plays."

"You always liked acting, didn't you?"

"Yeah. Ever since I was in 'A Funny Thing Happened On The Way to the Forum' in high school." We both laugh.

"What about Occupational Therapy?"

"We have arts and crafts. And we work with wood, metal, and so on. There are tools that we learn to use. We also do cooking, mostly baking cookies, and we learn how to plan a meal, do a wash. Everyday kinds of things."

"Sounds quite practical."

"It is. We were even taught how to write a résumé the other day."

"What about Group Therapy? I suppose you sit around and each person discusses his problems."

"Well, that's partly it. We work with a counselor—Miss Stone, the social worker. Anyway, we sit in a group and we discuss the Day Hospital, personal problems, gripes, hangups, and so on. And there are certain rules we have to follow there, too."

"Like what?"

"No eating, no smoking, and no private conversations are allowed."

"It really sounds very interesting to me. You're getting to like the program, aren't you?"

"It's all right. But I sometimes get bored."

"Bored!" I am taken aback. "How can you possibly be bored with all those absorbing activities?"

"It's the sameness of it all. I'd rather be working," he adds.

"Owen, you will be working, eventually. But as the doctor has told you, it takes time. Your first priority now is to get completely well. Then you can get a job. And, when you're ready, go back to college. You'll have to learn what I've learned. Patience."

"I guess you're right," he says. "But I'd still rather be working."

On February tenth, during a routine visit to the psychiatrist, we discover an incipient problem. I mention something to him that has been troubling me.

"It's his lips, doctor. He keeps making these mouthing movements, like this—" I try to imitate Owen, opening and closing my lips, stiffly.

"I see." The doctor looks quite concerned. "This could be the beginning of a very serious problem. I'm glad you're so observant."

"I thought it was significant. Otherwise I wouldn't have brought it up."

"This could be the precursor of serious side effects, namely, a condition called tardive dyskinesia. Usually tardive dyskinesia doesn't occur until after a patient has been on major tranquili-

zers for six months or more, but we have to change course. Its
effects on the brain are irreversible."

"What exactly is it?" I ask, anxiously.

"There are strange movements of the body, usually about the
tongue, lips, jaw, and face. The brain can be permanently
damaged."

"What do we do now?" Vince asks.

"We have to change the medication. Haldol is a very potent
drug."

"But it's been so effective," I say.

"Yes. But he's been on it for two months now. And he's over
the hill. We have to take precautionary measures and change
the medication."

"What will you give him instead?" Vince asks.

"Thorazine again. Or, if you prefer," he looks directly at me,
"chlorpromazine, the generic drug."

"Yes, I do," I say, "and we may still have some of it at
home."

"I'll give you a new prescription, anyway," the doctor states.
"He will take one hundred milligrams of chlorpromazine per
day, plus two milligrams of Cogentin. Oh, and let me add some
choline dihydrogen citrate to that. Here are your prescriptions
and your new schedule." He hands them to Owen.

"Thanks," Owen says. Needless to say, after this discussion,
he doesn't look at all too happy.

None of us does.

The doctor tries to soften the mood of the evening. He speaks
to Owen. "Except for this setback, your progress has been quite
good."

"I feel all right," Owen says.

But, tonight, disconsolation is the prevailing mood for us all.

I can no longer sleep. And when I do fall off into unconscious-
ness, it isn't the restful slumber of the past. It is fitful. Short-
lived. For there have been four months now. Four months of
anxiety and tension. I close my eyes. And try not to think of the
turmoil. The setbacks.

————

"I'm very depressed."

"Describe your symptoms."

"I feel terribly blue."

"What else do you feel?"

"That there's no hope."

"I see. And what would you like me to do?"

"Give me some of your magic."

"What do you mean by magic?"

"Drugs. Something miraculous."

"What do you consider to be miraculous?"

"Lithium. Lithium carbonate."

"All right," the doctor says, "but I want you to promise me one thing."

"What is that?"

"That you will take the lithium for at least one month."

"Yes, Dr. Glenn. You can be sure of that," I tell him. "All I want is to feel happy again. That's all. . . ."

I watch Owen closely now. Tardive dyskinesia. Even the name is sickening. Why, I wonder, in the depths of my current depression, can't the healing process itself go smoothly? Why?

I watch Owen closely. Whenever he isn't looking, I sneak a glance at his face, particularly his mouth. Is he making those strange, smacking movements? I stare. And stare.

The change of medication seems to be the solution. For within a day or so, I notice that the stiff, uncontrollable mouth movements have ceased. Another hurdle has been passed. The fear fades. And the depression, which it has left in its wake, dwindles, day by day, and finally dies. . . . Lithium is as effective as Thorazine.

"Your mouth looks perfectly fine now," I tell Owen, later, so that he will no longer be concerned. "You're not smacking your lips together anymore."

"I never noticed it in the first place," he tells me.

The routine with the Day Hospital continues. Each day I drop Owen off at nine-thirty and call for him at three-thirty. He goes in rather reluctantly, but always comes out smiling and relaxed, usually with one of his fellow patients. Like Owen, they are almost all young, mostly in their teens and twenties. I see them as they come out each day. Solitary figures. Only a few are called for by a parent. The others walk alone, to public transportation.

There is Lana, for example. Young, and very pretty, Lana was in the Long Island Medical Center with Owen. He met her up in O-P, where she was a patient for many weeks. Like so many of the other young patients, Lana is depressed. She cannot find herself. Cannot hold a job. And like most of the others, she lives away from her family. Alienated. Sustained on powerful medication.

"Can you give Lana a lift?" Owen wants to know. They have come out together.

"Of course," I reply. "Where are you going?"

"Oh, I don't want to take you out of your way," she says. "You can just drop me off at the park. I live just across the street."

And so, several times after that, Lana squeezes into the front seat of the car with us, and we drop her off in front of the park. "Be careful," I warn, before she crosses the busy highway. It is the medication that I am concerned about. The shots she gets once a month. I worry about Lana, too.

We are in Dr. Glenn's office again. It is February twenty-fourth. We arrive punctually, and as is his usual practice, Dr. Glenn calls Owen in for his private session first. When that is over, about a half hour later, he calls Vincent and me in and we all have a group conference.

"Good news!" the doctor beams. "Owen is almost completely well now. In fact, he's the best he's ever been."

"That's wonderful," Vince says, smiling.

I am smiling, also. The warmth of the doctor's words have been more effective than any known medication.

"Do you know," Dr. Glenn continues, looking straight at Owen, "that you were the sickest patient I ever had at Northview? Did you know that?"

"No," Owen replies, "I guess I didn't."

"I suppose you can't remember the Haldol bombardment," the doctor reminisces, holding his hands in front of him, fingers touching, "how we gave you shots every hour on the hour."

Owen shakes his head, "Nope."

"It's the amnesia," the doctor explains. "An expected reaction to psychosis."

"I'm very pleased with his progress, too," I state. "He rarely smokes cigars now—and he never talks about the Russians."

"And even if he did," the doctor reminds me, "it wouldn't be a problem."

But Owen has other concerns at this time. He has told Dr. Glenn, in private, that he has not yet fully regained his powers of concentration. He wonders how this will affect his future college performance.

Dr. Glenn, unabashedly, mentions Owen's private concern to us, and I am somewhat embarrassed that he should violate a confidence in this manner.

The doctor again stresses, to Vince and me, the importance of time in the healing process.

"Don't you see," he now turns to Owen, "that marijuana alone could have impaired your ability to concentrate. This is something that the average pot-smoking student doesn't realize. In your case, with all that heavy marijuana smoking, and the angel dust thrown in, the dopamine level in your brain was altered. Now it's slowly getting back to the correct level. You're making fine progress. But remember, it takes time."

it takes time . . .

TIME . . . Little by little. Hour by hour. Day by day. The healing continues. Owen gradually regains his powers of concentration. He is reading for longer and longer periods of time, and he is reading for a purpose. For now he is in the process of choosing a new college. He narrows his selection down to a superb university on Long Island. It has the most stringent requirements, a select student body, an excellent faculty. And a lovely location. Owen sends out his application.

But, he is increasingly bored at the Day Hospital. It is probably a good sign, for as he becomes progressively better, it is more and more difficult for him to be with people with problems. Nevertheless, I find it distressing, for it is still the only thing that he can do, the only place that he can be, at this time.

"Please," I urge each day, "please go in. It's the best thing for you right now."

And he looks at me with a look that says, who needs this?

On this particular day, I drop Owen off, as usual, in front of the mental health building, and go on to work. At midday I phone the Day Hospital, since the social worker, Miss Stone, wishes to speak with me. She's been wanting to arrange a meeting with me, and I've simply been unable to find the time. I call her back, hoping to have an interview with her on the telephone.

"How's Owen doing today?" I ask.

"Why, he's not here," she replies.

"How can that be?" I ask. My heart is now palpitating. "I dropped him off myself, this morning."

"Believe me," she says, "he has not been here at all today."

"What shall I do?" I ask, in despair.

And Miss Stone, the social worker, hasn't the vaguest idea.

I hang up and sit back in my chair. I decide, first and foremost, not to panic. Call the doctor? What will he be able to do? I must think. Clearly. Owen is playing hookey. He pretended to go into the building this morning, for my benefit. But he never got beyond the door. Why? And where has he gone? My clear flow of thought is now polluted. By the muddiness of panic. Shall I call the police? Oh, no. That would be a terrible thing to do. For all of us. I must think clearly. Logically. Owen is much better. If he is much better, then he is rational. If he is rational, then he knows that I will be back at the Day Hospital at three-thirty to pick him up. Therefore, I conclude, it will be very foolish for me to go to the hospital now. It is only one o'clock. I will wait until three-thirty. My cool-headed logic surprises even me. My mind stands firm. But my body is quaking.

At three-thirty, as I am driving down the major highway which fronts the hospital, I see a solitary figure, in jeans and brown jacket, walking along the center island of the road, toward the hospital. As I get closer, I think it is—yes! it is!—Owen! I noisily blow my horn and reduce my speed, waving frantically to him as I decelerate. He spots me, begins to run, and catches up with the car. I stop near the corner. Fortunately, the light has now changed to red, and the driver behind me is not a tailgater. I breathe a long sigh of relief as I open the door and Owen climbs into the back seat. Then, with him safely ensconced inside, I turn the car around, and head for home.

"You gave me quite a scare today," I tell him, later.

"Sorry about that," he replies.

"Where on earth did you go?"

"To the library."

"The library?"

"Yes."

"How did you know where the library was?"

"I just walked a couple of blocks from the hospital and—there it was."

"Owen, why did you go to the library?"

"I felt like reading."

"You felt like reading? But you could have gone to our local library. Why did you disappear like that? Didn't you think I might find out? That I might worry?"

"I said I'm sorry."

"Why did you do that?"

"Because I'm bored."

"Bored? With such a full, varied program?"

"Yes. I'm bored. I want to go back to work."

"But you will be going back to work. Eventually."

"Well, eventually isn't soon enough for me."

"We'll have to speak to Dr. Glenn about that," I say. It is useless to pursue the conversation. I am getting nowhere. And I am too shaken up to continue.

"So, you want to go to work," the doctor says, eyes piercing Owen.

"Yes."

"You will be able to. Very soon."

"How soon?"

"Well, your progress has been quite good. I'd say in a couple of months."

"I'll be getting my old job back this spring. Will I be able to work then?"

"Where is your old job?"

"In the state park. I worked there all last summer. It's a very pleasant job."

"Sounds excellent. Being outdoors will do you a world of good. However, you will have to watch out for the sun."

"What do you mean?" I ask. Has the sun I worship turned on us?

"Sunlight and Thorazine don't mix. He may develop an allergic reaction. The problem can easily be solved if he wears a hat."

"Will he be able to drive?" I ask. "The park is several miles from our home."

"Yes. He should be able to drive at that time."

"But what about the effects of the medication on him?"

"No problem," the doctor insists. "The medication has been reduced sufficiently. You know," he continues, in a pensive way, "Thorazine's a funny drug. If you were to take it, in a normal state of mind, its only effect would be to slow you down. I remember the case of a patient once who was taking Thorazine when he didn't really need it. He would get onto the highway and drive at twenty miles an hour. Why, he didn't even know he was doing only twenty. Yes, Thorazine can do strange things to you. . . ."

"Mother! Look! It's the SST!" Owen spots it in the sky. It is swooping down over us, lower and lower, like a graceful silver bird.

"Will you look at it!" Owen exclaims. He is seated in the back of the car, and yet, from his poor vantage point, he has noticed it first.

I peer through the windshield, and lo and behold! there it is! Pointed nose, slim, tapered body, looking like an elegant seagull swooping lower and lower above the foamy waves, this beautiful mechanical bird descends—the infamous SST.

"How lovely it is," I marvel to Owen. My eyes fill with tears, for a multiplicity of reasons. . . .

Once, it nows seems so long ago, Owen had mentioned the SST to me, had thought in his then-psychotic state that I had flown on it. And now, in full command of his faculties, he really sees it . . . and I really see it . . . the elegant SST. How marvelous is the regenerative power of the human brain. . . .

I turn to the left now, and watch as the plane descends in the direction of Kennedy Airport.

"I'm feeling wonderful," I tell the doctor.
"That's good to hear."
"Yes. And I've decided to stop the lithium."
"Why stop if it's helped you?"
"I've been taking it for a month. That's all I needed."
"It would be nice if you could continue."
"No need. Things are looking up."

My depression has been checked. The drug has worked its magic spell. But, more importantly, Owen's recovery, his happy, handsome face, his old charming manner, has been the real magic, the real antidote to my gloom. He is himself once more. And I am myself.

Vincent now takes Owen out for practice driving sessions in the car. He has not driven for six months.

From the beginning of January until the end of March, Owen continues as a patient in the Day Hospital. He attends regularly because he realizes that it is only a temporary thing. He feels very well now. His mood is consistently happy. And so is mine. For there's a touch of spring in the air.

One day, as I am parked at the Day Hospital, waiting for Owen to emerge, he comes out, carrying a large healthy plant.

"Wherever did you get that?" I ask, pleased as can be, for plants are my passion.

"In the hospital greenhouse. We had a tour today, and they let anyone who was interested choose a plant to take home."

I take the plant from him. "Why, it's an aloe," I tell him, as he gets into the car. "An *Aloe vera.*"

"It has certain healing properties, as I understand it," Owen states.

"Yes. The sap from its leaves can be used as an ointment for burns. In fact, it has been nicknamed the burn plant."

"Pretty clever."

"Yes." I start the engine. "This was a very thoughtful present. Plants always make me very happy for they are living, growing, beautiful things."

"I know, Mother. That's why I brought it to you."

The snows of a harsh winter melt, the thermometer progressively rises, and with it, Owen's hopes. He is waiting to hear about his old summer job.

Finally, Owen receives word. The parks department would like him back and they have assigned him to a lovely park only a few miles from our home.

He is beaming now. "It's terrific," he states. "I'll be able to work for four months. Just think of all the money I'll be able to save."

"That's true."

"Listen, you and Dad are going to have three kids in universities this coming year."

"I know."

"So, every little bit helps. Besides, I'll be out in the fresh air every day, not down in a dingy basement."

"Yes," I smile. "It will really be a pleasant change, won't it?"

"I can't wait."

"I am happy for you, Owen. I really and truly am."

That evening he speaks to his father.

"I'll need the car every day now," he says.

"You can drop me off at the station in the morning and take mine," Vince tells him.

"But, please," I caution, "I want you to drive very carefully." I cannot help it, but I am still concerned because of the medication.

"You don't have to worry about me," he grins. "I took Driver Education."

And so, Owen begins to work, and his spirits, like mine, are clearly on the upswing. Each day he comes home, ruddy-cheeked and smiling. He is once more a productive human being, and what is even better, he is making money. He works now with such enthusiasm that he is soon promoted to a supervisory position. We are all very proud of him.

In mid-April, there is further, and more important, good news. Owen has been accepted for admission to the university of his choice, here on Long Island. He shows me the certificate of admission.

"Oh! I am so happy. So happy."

"I will be starting classes the end of August."

"So soon?"

"Yes."

"Well," I tell him, "that means we have a lot of planning to do."

I speak to Vince that evening.

"We have to find a house now."

And now the road is straight and clear. We know exactly where to look for a house. We will find one close to the campus. For Owen will no longer live in a dorm. He will now live at home.

22

SPRING

The unusually harsh Long Island winter expires. It is spring now. As I wake up on this sleepy Sunday, I rejoice in the realization of spring. For I have seen tiny chartreuse buds shyly opening on the pin oak outside my window. And today, in one of its branches, a young bird chirps, merrily. The white hazy winter sky has turned pure, unpolluted blue. And the warmth, the promise, is in the air.

Wake up, I tell myself. It's all right now. The nightmare is ended. Finis. And yet, it really wasn't a nightmare, I remind myself. Nightmares are only bad dreams. And this was real. More real than any dream can ever be. Perhaps Owen faintly remembers it as only a bad dream, for

> to the person in the bell jar, blank and stopped as
> a dead baby, the world itself is the bad dream—

And I think once more of mass suicides and murders, on the death of poets, and I know that Sylvia Plath was correct. The world itself is a bad dream.

Owen is no longer in the bell jar of madness. He has been freed by the wonders of modern medicine. And the bad dream, the eerie unreality of it, is ended. For all of us.

I stretch out, lazily, in bed, on this sunny morning, listening to Vince putter in the kitchen. It's been a long time between sleepy Sundays. . . .

But, today I will not luxuriate in my laziness. Today there will be no time for sleeping. For we have just found a house. A lovely house. New and spacious, it is situated on a heavily wooded half-acre only four miles from the university Owen will attend. Today we are taking the children out to see it. And soon, when summer comes, we will leave our cramped, inadequate apartment.

I get up and open the window wide. A mild April breeze stirs the sheer curtains. The warmth of spring enters, flooding the room with sunlight.

There is a knock on the door, a pause, and Owen comes in.

"Hi, Mom. Glad I didn't wake you. Are we going out to the new house today?"

"We certainly are. I'll be ready in a few minutes."

He leaves, a delighted grin on his face.

Spring. I remember other happy spring mornings. Full of joy. And promise.

EPILOGUE

It is exactly one year now since Owen was discharged from the hospital.

He is currently enrolled as a full-time student in a fine university on Long Island. He is a Political Science major. For he has always been a student of history.

He lives at home, commuting to college by car each day. We are close to the university.

His Thorazine pills sit, untouched now, on the shelf. Although the doctor recommends a small daily maintenance dose, Owen has decided that he no longer needs this medication, and refuses to take it. He also refuses to take vitamins. Owen is not a pill-popper.

Dr. Glenn is there, should Owen wish to see him. At the moment, there is no need. Perhaps there will never be a need.

Owen is involved with music now. He has a new stereo and a growing record collection. He also plays the piano and the guitar every single day. And he sings, in his rich, mellifluous voice.

He no longer smokes cigars.

And he no longer writes poetry.